BRITAIN'S
INDUSTRIAL
HERITAGE

written and photographed by
JOHN HANNAVY

First published in Great Britain in 2015

Text, photography, digital image restorations and design copyright © 2015 John Hannavy.
www.johnhannavy.co.uk

A CIP catalogue record for this book is available from the British Library.

John Hannavy has asserted his right under the Copyright, Designs and Patents Act 1988 to be identified as the author of this book.

ISBN 978 0 85710 093 1

PiXZ Books
Halsgrove House, Ryelands Business Park, Bagley Road, Wellington, Somerset TA21 9PZ
Tel: 01823 653777
Fax: 01823 216796
email: sales@halsgrove.com

An imprint of Halstar Ltd, part of the Halsgrove group of companies
Information on all Halsgrove titles is available at: www.halsgrove.com

Printed and bound in China by Everbest Printing Co Ltd

Front cover image: The restored headgear at The Big Pit, Blaenafon, the National Mining Museum of Wales.
Title page image: Looking up the chimney of one of the large furnaces at Blaenafon Ironworks.
Contents page image: Narrow boats negotiating the Caen Hill flight of locks on the Kennet and Avon Canal, Wiltshire.

By the same author:
Edwardian Mining In Old Postcards
The Once-Ubiquitous Paddle Steamer
Preserved Steam-Powered Machines

CONTENTS

INTRODUCTION

BRITAIN'S INDUSTRIAL HERITAGE draws us to historic sites in our millions every year. There seems to be no limit to our fascination with working cotton mills, preserved coal mines, steam railways, and the thousand-and-one other evocative reminders of the country's industrial past.

above: The Australian-built replica of Captain Cook's HMB *Endeavour* visiting Falmouth in 1990.

It was not always like this. As recently as the 1960s, at the same time as Dr Beeching was promising that steam trains would never again run on British railway lines, much of the country's rich industrial heritage was simply rotting away.

Canals had been all but abandoned – their banks collapsing and overgrown with weeds, their locks filled with rubbish. Some had already been filled in to make way for motorways and railways.

opposite: Redundant weights, Anderton Boat Lift, Cheshire.

Hundreds of textile mills across the country – no longer competitive in the face of cheaper imports – stood empty and crumbling, much of their equipment exported to the same countries whose lower wage structures had brought about their downfall. Many of those which were still operating were struggling to make ends meet and faced with a gloomy future.

Abandoned ironworks, corn mills, pumping stations and airfields were all suffering similarly. Except for a few dedicated enthusiasts, visiting them was not yet really part of our culture. I admit to having been one of those enthusiasts – and still am – who like nothing better than exploring abandoned sites and photographing them.

below: Manchester's Liverpool Road Station in1966.

bottom: The Lancashire & Yorkshire Railway fines book.

Fifty years after I first ventured out with my camera, many of the abandoned sites of my youth have long since been cleared and replaced. Many others, thankfully, are abandoned no more.

Today, Manchester's Liverpool Road Station – the first purpose-built passenger railway station in the world – is reborn, its vast warehouses, some of which date from the reign of King William IV, restored to their original magnificence.

In 1966 when I first visited, the buildings had been pretty much abandoned for more than a generation, but it was still clearly a railway station. The ticket office behind its little window was in darkness, but the door was ajar, and too tempting to ignore. Inside, in what had probably been the Station Master's office, an ancient book lay abandoned on a

right: An early
London General
double decker bus.
Such vehicles were
introduced in the
early Edwardian
years, the heyday of
the picture postcard,
and the new buses
were the subjects of
an extensive series of
cards, now prized by
postcard collectors.

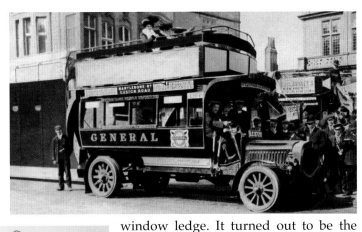

above: At the Beamish
Open Air Museum in
Northumberland, a
modern interpretation
of a London General
bus – based on a later
model and mounted
on a modern vehicle
chassis – gives visitors
an alternative to the
tramcar when making
their way around the
site.

window ledge. It turned out to be the Lancashire & Yorkshire Railway's local fines book, which detailed every transgression punishable by a fine over a period of many years. The L&YR had been formed in 1847 after the amalgamation of several smaller companies, and operated until subsumed into the LMS when the big four railway groupings were established in 1923. Had the book lain there for half a century when I saw it? I have often wondered, in the decades since, what happened to it.

Twenty years later, I was back in those same station buildings and warehouses – which had by then become The Greater Manchester Museum of Science and Industry – presenting a television series on the history of photography for the BBC, and using some of the many early cameras and optical equipment in the museum's collection. Now known simply as MOSI (Museum of Science and Industry) the museum is housed in five listed buildings, and covers just about every aspect of the city's history.

The transformation of so many derelict sites into award-winning museums since the 1970s has, of course, been driven by the huge growth in leisure industries, itself powered by the ubiquity of the car. We all own cars, we all want to use them for days out, and where better to go than somewhere where we can connect with the working lives and the living conditions of our ancestors.

Perhaps those ancestors would be amused at our willingness to make our way through underground tunnels in preserved coal, tin and copper mines, heads bowed, hard hats on, but they too found such working conditions fascinating.

A century ago, the market for picture postcards of industrial sites was very much greater than it is today. Every industrial town worth its salt would have dozens, if not hundreds of different postcards on sale, covering every aspect of the working lives of its community. Several of these postcards will be used alongside my own original photography in the following pages.

Obviously in a volume this size, there will be a lot of omissions – and some will no doubt question my choices as to which sites are included and illustrated. The challenge has been in determining which of my favourites, when illustrated together, offer a sense of the 'bigger picture'.

The challenge has also been to establish a time frame for inclusion, for it could be argued that the first seeds of industrialisation were planted millennia ago. Were no boundaries established, the book would become little more than a listing.

With only a few exceptions, therefore, the locations selected for inclusion and discussion in these pages have been selected from those which came to prominence during the 18th to 21st centuries.

below: One of the first suspension road bridges in the world, Thomas Telford's beautiful bridge over the River Conwy was completed in 1826. Standing just below the battlements of Conwy Castle, it originally carried the main road, but is now preserved by the National Trust and accessible to pedestrians only.

left: An early 20th century tinted postcard of the Phoenix & Clifton Ironworks in Coatbridge. The production of tinted postcards pre-Great War was a costly business, so projected sales of cards like this must have been considerable to warrant the expenditure.

The selection has also largely been informed by the thematic structure of the book, but if including a site helps tell the story more effectively, I hope I have given it a mention.

The whole question of just when industrialisation actually started has no categorical answer. To some historians it started when machines first played an important part in human life and commerce – but how do we define a machine? To others it was when manufacturing processes moved from small-scale operations employing one family, to centralised production facilities employing large numbers of people.

With the first definition in mind, industrialisation goes back to Roman times at the latest, when the corn mill was introduced – using a water-powered machine to grind corn.

Using the second definition, industrialisation would start with the development of sites like Coalbrookdale and the beginnings of what we know today as the Industrial Revolution.

As is always the case with a book like this, the author's name, given prominence on the cover conceals the input of many other people whose expertise has added to the story. To all the curators and heritage site managers and guides who have assisted me, and to those friends who have pointed me towards fascinating images, my grateful thanks. Thanks too, of course, to my wife, Kath, for her constant support.

John Hannavy 2015

opposite page: Seeing the complex lens of the Lighthouse on Portland is the reward for a dizzying climb up to the top inside the tower. The Fresnel lens assembly is made up of several hundred carefully aligned prismatic sections. In the late 1780s Portland was the first British lighthouse to use a lens system rather than just reflectors, projecting its powerful beam much further out to sea, and using fewer lamps to do so.

above: A group of apprentices at the Linthouse shipyard of Andrew Steven & Sons of Govan in 1907. The company had opened a new engine and boiler works in a custom-built facility in 1871.

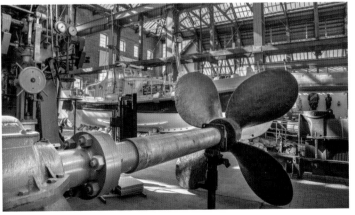

left: The Linthouse Engine Building was dismantled and rebuilt at Girvan, now housing the Scottish Maritime Museum.

9

WIND & WATER POWER

THE HARNESSING OF WIND AND WATER POWER in Britain predates the Industrial Revolution by about fifteen hundred years.

The most frequently-found industrial relic is probably the corn mill – the focal point of every agricultural community, and a key component of the food supply chain. The introduction of the mill, some two millennia ago, would have been one of the first instances where centralised processing of farm produce took place.

opposite: Saxtead Green Post Mill rotated so the sails faced into the wind.

The mill's location was dictated by geography. Ideally it needed to be near the farming community whose corn it ground, near the community who bought and used its flour, and located close by a plentiful supply of water.

above: The Elizabethan corn mill at Dunham Massey, Cheshire

The first mills in Britain were probably what are known today as 'Norse mills' and examples are still to be found in the Orkney and Shetland Islands and in the Western Isles of Scotland – several very primitive examples of these under-driven mills can be found on the island of Lewis. The design was very simple – a stream of fast moving water rotated rudimentary paddle wheels beneath the mill floor, directly turning the millstone above. Such mills were in use over 2000 years ago, being easy to construct with only basic expertise. However, they were inefficient, requiring a substantial supply of water, and by the nature of their direct-drive, could power only one pair of grindstones.

below: Dounby Click Mill, a restored Norse Mill on the Orkney Mainland.

Some mills could depend on the natural force of the water to turn the grindstone, but where the water flow was weak or unreliable, it was collected and stored in large ponds. When needed, it was directed through narrowing channels to increase its flow before eventually passing under the mill and driving the rotor.

The Romans introduced 'Vitruvian' over-shot or bucket mills, but perhaps surprisingly, much medieval development went into the refinement of the undershot wheel – where the flow propelled the bottom blades of the waterwheel.

In Winchester – where there has been a

mill on the River Itchen since medieval times – the undershot City Mill has been restored to full working order by the National Trust and since 2004 is once again grinding corn.

Undershot wheels were fine when rivers were in flood and the water flow was considerable, but tended to be at their least efficient in the dry autumn weeks when the corn was ready to be ground. The fast-flowing Itchen, however, rarely caused problems.

Where such issues were likely to arise, water needed to be conserved and stored for when it was needed, and that requirement led to the development of the millpond, or in some cases, a series of ponds sited successively higher above the mill.

More efficient was the breastshot design, where water was introduced via a narrowing mill lade to fall on to the blades of the wheel at axle level, combining water power with the natural forces of gravity.

This proved to be much more successful than the undershot wheel, with the same quantity of water producing over double the power.

But it was the overshot wheel – where water was introduced at the top of the wheel – which drove the majority of later mills, and many of the water-powered 'manufactories' of the Industrial Revolution.

The overshot mill was a refinement of the ancient bucket mill, where water was poured into troughs on the wheel, the weight of the water providing the rotative power. There was often sufficient power from a large overshot

left: A quern lies against the wall of Nether Alderley Mill in Cheshire. There has been a mill on this site since the late 13th century, but the present mill, restored and operated by the National Trust, dates from the 16th.

below: The overshot wheel at New Abbey Corn Mill in Dumfriesshire.

wheel to drive more than one pair of stones, some wheels driving three or more pairs to meet the ever-growing demand for flour.

Almost double the power was achieved at the tandem-wheel Nether Alderley Mill in Cheshire, where two overshot wheels – each of them driving several separate pairs of grindstones – were rotated by the same water flow, the first wheel emptying its water into the buckets of the second.

Coastal mills were amongst the first to exploit tidal power – the earliest known date from the 6th century at the latest. But it was not wave power which they employed – water from the incoming tide was stored in large ponds, to be released once the tide had fallen sufficiently to create a robust flow out from the ponds.

It is estimated that there were once as many as two hundred tide mills operating around Britain's coast, a third of them in and around London.

Only two remain intact. At Woodbridge in Suffolk, one of them has been restored to full working order. The other is Eling Tide Mill in Hampshire, and both are open to the public.

There has been a mill on the site at Woodbridge, originally powered by water from the River Deben, since the 12th century, but the present tide mill dates from the late 18th.

Water from the 7-acre reservoir powered a 5m diameter

opposite top: The tail-race of Winchester City Mill.

middle: An undershot wheel at Preston Mill in East Linton.

bottom: Wooden machinery in the late 19th century over-shot Tormiston Mill at Stenness on the Orkney Mainland. A 4m diameter iron wheel drove three pairs of millstones.

13

right: Woodbridge
Tide Mill, Suffolk, a
five-storey clapper-
boarded building
dating from the
18th century, with a
beautiful mansard or
boudle-pitched roof.

below left: Skidby
Windmill near
Beverley, a tower
mill dating from
1821, heightened in
1870.

below right: The
fantail of Thorpness
Wind Pump – a post
mill in Suffolk, with
the former water
tower beyond.

oak undershot wheel which drove three pairs of stones, but in its restored state, a much smaller reservoir has been created – the original now being a marina.

Windmills, now a relative rarity and tourist magnet in some parts of the country, were once found throughout Britain. Even the surviving few – some restored and once again milling flour, albeit for the benefit of visitors rather than as a commercial undertaking – exemplify the rich variety of designs which were developed to meet the growing need for both flour and animal feed.

The most common form of early windmill was the post mill – known as a peg mill in the north of England – where the entire wooden mill building rotated around a central post, ensuring the sails were always facing the wind for maximum efficiency. The rotating building, known as the 'buck', contained all the milling machinery, and was accessed by a steep wooden staircase, the bottom edge of which ran on rails which encircled the mill. As the wind direction changed, the spinning fantail provided sufficient energy to rotate the buck. Beneath the buck was a stone or brick building through which the post rose. These mills were being built as early as the 13th century, and once numbered many hundreds throughout England. Several restored examples are regularly open to visitors.

Smock mills have been known in England since the early 17th century at the latest, and like post mills, were wooden-bodied. With a smock mill, however, only the cap carrying the sails and fantail rotated, the rest of the building being firmly rooted to the ground. The smock mill at Lacey Green in

above left: The steep wooden staircase which gave access to the buck at Saxtead Green Post Mill in Suffolk.

above: Eastbridge Wind Pump, seen here silhouetted against a stormy sky, is a restored 'smock mill' built in the mid 19th century to drain Minsmere Levels near Leiston in Suffolk, one of hundreds of mills which helped drain the Fenlands. Ruinous by 1977, it was dismantled and moved to the Museum of East Anglian Life at Stowmarket where it was restored.

The huge Laxey Wheel, at 22m diameter the world's largest water wheel, was designed by Robert Casement. Revolving at only 3rpm, it drained the deep mines where up to 600 miners excavated lead, copper, silver and zinc ores until the mines closed in 1929. The *Lady Isabella* wheel was restored in the 1960s and is now a major tourist site.

Buckinghamshire can trace its origins back to around 1650, and a fine example from the early 19th century – Killick's Mill at Meopham in Kent – is also open to the public.

Both wind and water power were used to produce direct drive to corn mills, sawmills, or a hundred other industrial applications – pumps being the most common.

Water powered the huge Laxey Wheel pump in the Isle of Man, the biggest water wheel in the world – known as *Lady Isabella* and built in 1854 – which drained the local mines.

Its water came from reservoirs located up in the hills at a higher elevation than the top of the wheel, creating sufficient pressure to raise the water up the tower and over the top of the overshot wheel.

left: Haigh WInd Pump near Wigan in Lancashire, a tower mill built in 1845, pumped water from a deep aquifer to a reservoir for use at nearby Haigh Brewery. In 2011, the windmill was awarded Lottery funding to effect a cosmetic restoration of what is now the last windmill in Lancashire.

One of the more revolutionary uses of water power was first installed to serve one of the country's great 19th century country houses – a hydro-electric system.

As befitting a man of great wealth, Sir William Armstrong built himself a fishing lodge near Rothbury in Northumberland.

Armstrong's engineering works at Elswick, opened in 1847, manufactured everything from cranes and bridges to armaments. He had established his credentials during the Crimean War, 1854-56, developing and manufacturing a lighter and much more versatile field gun for the British Army.

Heavier guns followed, and by the end of the decade Armstrong guns were the artillery weapons of choice for the British government. All of which made Sir William a very wealthy man indeed. Add to that his other achievements including engineering the Tyne Swing Bridge, and Armstrong's fame was already spreading far and wide.

The fishing lodge, Cragside, set in the most magnificent wooded landscape, grew over the years to become a magnificent mansion, but it was Armstrong's fascination with Joseph Swan's experiments with electricity which led, in 1879, to Cragside becoming the first house in the world to be illuminated by incandescent lamps, the system powered by one of Britain's first hydro-electric schemes.

below: The large breast-shot wheel at Cheddleton Flint Mill stands just a few yards from the Caldon Canal in Staffordshire. Ground flint was an essential component in the production of creamware pottery.

17

right: Stanley Mills, a huge complex of cotton mills built by the Duke of Atholl in a part of Scotland better known for wool, used the waters of the River Tay to power the machinery. The Tay is Britain's fastest-flowing river, and at Stanley it is flowing at its fastest. In the late 18th century, water-power was the most efficient way of driving machinery. The river offered a commercial advantage which outweighed the remoteness of the location, and its distance from the west coast ports where the bulk of cotton was imported.

opposite top: A narrow overshot iron wheel generated hydraulic power for the Cragside estate.

far right middle: The switch room at Cragside's hydro-electric power station at Burnfoot.

bottom right: The National Trust's recreation of Joseph Swan's vase light bulb.

bottom left: Today the Generating Room at Cragside contains an 1881 Gilkes water turbine, and the 1883 Crompton generator.

Parts of the house had been fitted with carbon arc lamps as early as 1878, powered by a small water turbine which was fed by waters from Debden Lake, with power generated by a Siemens dynamo being relayed to the house along nearly a mile of cable. When the arc lights were not needed, the water was diverted to operate the estate's sawmill. A major step forward took place in 1879 with the first of Swan's lamps installed.

The first room to be illuminated by Swan lamps was the library, and Armstrong wrote to the journal *The Engineer* about the system in January 1881, by which time there were over forty-five such lamps in the house. In his letter, he described the eight lamps in the library – four in a large globe suspended from the ceiling, and four others each built into ornate vases. Armstrong wrote:

The vases, being enamel on copper, are themselves conductors, and serve for carrying the return current from the incandescent carbon to a metallic case in connection with the main return wire. The entering current is brought by a branch wire to a small insulated mercury cup in the centre of the base, and is carried forward to the lamp by a piece of insulated wire which passes through the interior of the lamp on the top. The protruding end of this wire is naked, and dips into the mercury cup when the vase is set down. Thus the lamp may be extinguished and relighted at pleasure merely by removing the vase from its seat or setting it down again.

Hardly the safest of systems, but health and safety considerations were still many decades in the future.

The National Trust has recreated the lamps, but embodied a very much safer switching system than Swan employed!

Armstrong embraced electricity enthusiastically, replacing the turbines and dynamos when the demand for electricity required a greater output – all these improvements taking place in a bigger powerhouse he had built on his estate at Burnfoot in 1886 and fitted out with a Gilkes turbine, and a Crompton generator. The new powerhouse was fed with water from Nelly's Moss Lakes over 300 feet above it, and could generate almost 18kw of electricity. All this was supervised twenty-four hours a day by the grandly-titled *'Caretaker of the Electric Light'*. The generator, designed in 1883, is still in situ today.

The dynamo was capable of generating 90 amps of 110 volt direct current, but even that soon proved insufficient to meet peak demand from the house. So, in the mid 1890s, a battery room and a second dynamo room were added to the power house, the former filled with an array of huge lead-acid batteries, each weighing nearly one hundredweight. They were charged at times of reduced demand, and then drawn upon to meet peaks, or when the water flow was insufficient to operate the dynamo at full capacity.

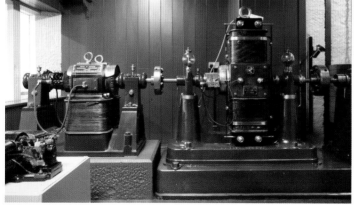

CANALS: SAILING OVER HILLS

THE CANAL REVOLUTION was one of the many important components of the great industrial revolution which turned Britain from a largely agricultural economy into a world powerhouse.

Without a more effective means of transporting large quantities of heavy manufactured goods than horse-drawn wagons, industrial development would never have expanded in the way it did.

The idea was not entirely new – rivers had been being dredged, widened and re-routed since the 16th century at the latest to improve navigation, but the idea of an entirely artificial waterway did not come into being until the 18th century when Thomas Steers constructed the Newry Canal in Northern Ireland.

The first true canal on mainland Britain was the Bridgewater Canal, commissioned by the Duke of Bridgewater as an aid to transporting coal from his mines into the city of Manchester.

The man he chose for the job was engineer James Brindley, whose name woud later become synonymous with some of the greatest canal-building projects covering the length and breadth of the country.

opposite top: The 16-flight central section of John Rennie's Caen Hill locks on the Kennet & Avon Canal,

opposite bottom: The 1812 Boulton & Watt beam engine at Crofton Pumping Station which pumped water into the highest section of the Kennet & Avon Canal.

above: A narrow boat in a cutting on the Chester & Ellesmere (now Shropshire Union) Canal, from a tinted postcard published c.1905.

left: An early 20th century excursion party pose for the camera c.1910. Their excursion had started at the legendary Wigan Pier, a coal wharf on the Leeds & Liverpool Canal.

right: *Tiger*, a fast canal boat with horse and crew on the Leeds & Liverpool Canal c.1900. Families usually lived on board their boats. Behind the two people at the stern can be seen the chimney of the stove which was used both to heat the little cabin, and cook the food. Despite the growing use of diesel-power in the 20th century, horse-drawn canal boats could still be seen along stretches of the narrower canals into the 1950s.

The Bridgewater Canal opened in 1761, and included what was considered one of the engineering marvels of its day – an aqueduct over the River Irwell.

The horse-drawn canal narrow-boats could carry thirty tons of coal at a time – more than six times what a single horse could pull on a road cart. That gave the Duke a huge commercial advantage, allowing him to reduce the cost of coal to Manchester businesses, while at the same time vastly increasing his profit margin per ton shipped. Such financial benefits outweighed the enormous construction costs and triggered a huge canal-building programme over the following half century.

below: Children playing on the Bridgewater Canal at Worsley Packet House in 1974. The orange colour of the canal water is due to minerals still being washed out from the Duke of Bridgewater's former mines.

It was a lengthy process building a canal – every project, like the railways a century later, required a specific Act of Parliament to authorise it, often also involving legal disputes about land ownership and rights of way. Despite the many obstacles, the idea of a canal network took hold relatively quickly.

The Bridgewater Canal, as originally built, was a 'contour' canal, levelling out the undulations of the landscape with cuttings and aqueducts, but when it was extended to Runcorn some means was necessary to lower the canal down to the level of the River Mersey.

By that time, Brindley had already introduced the idea of locks when building the Trent and Mersey Canal which had opened in 1776.

left: Fishing boats making their way through Telford's Caledonian Canal in the early 1900s are seen here, in a tinted postcard, passing Tomnahurich.

Brindley had a vision – that one day canals would link England's four great rivers, the Thames, Mersey, Trent and Severn, to allow canal boats to sail from coast to coast, and from north to south. In his lifetime he worked hard towards that dream, being personally responsible for the design and engineering of nearly 600km of waterways.

His dream had virtually been realised by the first quarter of the 19th century, thanks to the ingenuity of several great engineers – amongst them such eminent figures as Thomas Telford, one of the later engineers to enter the scene, and John Rennie.

While one of Telford's greatest achievements was undoubtedly the Caledonian Canal which opened up a shipping route between north-east and south-west Scotland by linking the lochs in the Great Glen, he was also responsible, with William Jessop, for the 110km Ellesmere Canal which linked the Mersey, the Dee and the Severn.

The most spectacular part of that canal is the 307m long Pontcysylite Viaduct which carries the Llangollen branch of the canal in a cast-iron trough over the Dee. Now known as the Llangollen Canal, it is a favourite location for narrow-boat holidaymakers, the sail across the viaduct 40m above the river valley being an unforgettable experience.

The Ellesmere Canal, together with the Birmingham & Liverpool Junction and the Chester Canal, is now part of what is known as the Shropshire Union.

below: John Rennie, from a contemporary engraving.

bottom: The Pump House at Ellesmere Port reflected in still waters, part of the huge dock complex designed by Thomas Telford on the Shropshire Union Canal. The docks are now home to the National Waterways Museum.

23

John Rennie's first canal project was the Lancaster Canal in the early 1790s, followed quickly by the Crinan Canal in the west of Scotland. His most spectacular achievement, however, was undoubtedly the 140km Kennet & Avon Canal in Wiltshire, with its remarkable flight of 29 locks lifting boats up and over Caen Hill towards Devizes. The canal took sixteen years to build, the final section being that long flight with its many feeder lagoons. It finally opened in 1810.

At first glance, any connection between John Rennie in the 1790s and the Nicholl Russell Studios in Dundee in the 1990s may not be obvious. But two centuries after John Rennie engineered the Caen Hill Locks, it was Nicholl Russell Studios who came up with the 21st century solution to taking boats over hills – the Falkirk Wheel.

While Rennie's flight of locks is now in its third century – the bicentenary of the canal's completion in 1810 was celebrated with new sets of lock gates – Scotland engineered the re-opening of the link between the Union Canal and the Forth & Clyde Canal with the construction of the world's most spectacular boat lift. Two very different solutions to exactly the same challenge, each of which was at the leading edge of technological achievement in its day.

top: Boats at the top of the 16-flight section of the Caen Hill rise.

above: The stern of a brightly painted narrow boat at the National Waterways Museum, Ellesmere Port.

The Falkirk Wheel, as you might expect from a 21st century solution, is much more sparing in its use of a canal's most important asset – water. While Rennie had to harness countless streams, and construct a series of lagoons to store water to refill each lock at Caen Hill, the Falkirk Wheel hardly wastes a drop! The two gondolas simply exchange water between the basin at the bottom of the wheel and the aqueduct at the top.

Ever since the first canals were built, engineers have faced the challenges of what to do with hills – should they tunnel through them, go around them, or go over them? Many of their solutions were highly original, so the magnificent Falkirk Wheel is simply the latest in more than two centuries of engineering innovation.

opposite page: The spectacular Falkirk Wheel boat lift, already a popular visitor attraction after only little more than a decade.

What marks it out as unique in Britain's canal history is that it is the first time that the aesthetics of the solution were considered to be just as important as the engineering itself.

In today's culture where leisure and tourist interests are high on the agenda, that is hardly surprising. That such a dramatic solution to the challenge of raising canal boats 20m up a hillside should also be one of the most environmentally friendly and energy efficient is remarkable indeed. The Falkirk Wheel attracts large numbers of visitors because of its novelty, but will, over the years, gradually take its place in the pantheon of heritage sites in 'future Britain'.

Scotland's Union Canal – connected to the top of the Falkirk Wheel – has no locks, but given Britain's undulating landscapes, few canal builders faced such a straightforward engineering challenge. Opened in 1822, it linked Scotland's capital with the Forth & Clyde Canal – originally known as the Great Canal – at Falkirk.

Canal builders have, over the centuries, come up with a range of means of raising and lowering boats, and while locks were by far the simplest to engineer, boat lifts were in use long before the Falkirk Wheel.

One of the oldest and most interesting is the 1875 Anderton Boat Lift which raised and lowered craft between the River Weaver and the Trent & Mersey Canal in Cheshire.

As originally built, the two caissons were so perfectly balanced that it required remarkably little hydraulic effort to operate the lift.

The original counter-balanced system was replaced in 1908 by electric power, but the lift, now computer-controlled, once again works hydraulically.

Intriguingly, today's state of the art computer system, together with the current health and safety obsession – and consideration for the age of the machinery – actually means it now takes more time and more people to operate the lift than it did a century and a quarter ago.

The Hay Inclined Plane was built in 1793 to move canal tub boats 63m up and down between the Shropshire Canal at Blists Hill to a short canal spur at Coalport and thence to the River Severn. Initially the energy was provided by a combination of gravity and men with ropes — while a boat descended full of coal, it was partly counter-balanced by an empty tub being raised on the other track — thus it was largely braking energy which was required. A steam engine took over much of the work in the 19th century, and the ruins of the engine house can still be seen at the top of the incline. The inclined plane did the work of a flight of around 16-20 locks. It took less than four minutes to lower a boat down to the bottom — a descent which would have taken three-four hours through locks. The system lowered its final boat in 1894 after just over a century of use, and was abandoned and the rails lifted in 1907. The current tracks use former British Railways metals to recreate the plane's original appearance.

Before boat lifts – and even before the use of locks was widespread – some canal builders came up with more unusual ways of moving boats between canals and rivers. With inclined planes, the boats were either floated on to wheel sets, or into water-filled caissons, and raised or lowered on rails.

Inclined planes have been in use for hundreds of years – probably first in China. One of the earliest on a British canal was the 1793-built 63m Hay Inclined Plane at Ironbridge in Shropshire. It was restored in the 1970s and is a spectacular survival.

Some were even built underground – on the Bridgewater Canal from 1795, boats were raised or lowered on a 1 in 4 gradient between underground tunnels in the Duke of Bridgewater's mines. Barges entered a lock, settled on to carriages, and were raised or lowered along counter-balanced rope-linked twin rail tracks.

It was the simple lock which, despite its extravagant use of water, became the normal means of raising and lowering canal boats. Brindley had established a width for the cut on the Bridgewater Canal, and that in turn dictated maximum boat size.

When it came to building the locks on the Runcorn extension, the size of the boats then dictated the necessary size and shape of the locks themselves. Within reasonable latitude, those measurements were replicated on numerous other 'narrow' canals.

Visitors to the National Waterways Museum in the 1990s watch as a British Waterways narrow boat exits from one of the locks on the Shropshire Union.

In 1966 when this picture was taken, the Rochdale Canal was all but abandoned, locks overflowing, and much of the canal clogged with weeds and discarded rubbish. Today the canal has been restored, the canalside has been transformed and is now popular with walkers and canal enthusiasts alike.

left: A view of the Wigan Pier basin on the Leeds & Liverpool Canal. A former goods warehouse has been converted into a pub and restaurant, while the stone repair sheds in the middle distance have been converted into office space. The whole area was derelict before renovation in the 1980s, and for twenty years was home to an intereactive heritage centre *The Way We Were*, which closed ten years ago.

below: A boat entering Dunardry Lock 13 on Rennie's Crinan Canal. The canal is now just used by pleasure craft.

There were some anomalous exceptions which would lead to the investors in a number of canals never achieving the profitability of which they dreamed.

One such was the Leeds & Liverpool Canal, the building of which started at both ends simultaneously in 1770. Shortage of cash, rather than engineering problems, however, brought construction work to a halt both at Wigan, and at Gargrave in Yorkshire in 1776.

The original Leeds-to-Gargrave section had been built to a different specification than the Liverpool to Wigan cut. While the canal from Wigan to the sea had standard 72 foot locks able to accommodate two narrow boats side by side or one wide boat, work had started from the Leeds end on locks only 60 feet long. To deal with this, the canal pioneered what became known as the 'short boat' – the same width as the standard canal barge used throughout the country, but 12 feet shorter.

It was that design decision which determined that, after its completion in 1816, the canal could never assume the role of major importance within the national waterways network which it should have done. While Leeds-Liverpool boats could move anywhere through the canal system, longer Midlands boats could not be accommodated in the trans-Pennine locks.

Despite the canal's name, and the fact that Liverpool's dockland was described in the 18th century as the finest complete dock system in the world, the original plans for the canal did not offer direct access to the docks at all. Indeed, it was well after completion that locks were eventually built joining canal and docks, and giving access from the Mersey to what was at the time one of the busiest waterways in the world. When those locks were completed – in 1848 – full size "wide boats" could sail direct from Birkenhead on the other side of the Mersey, straight through to Wigan.

While the horse drawn cart could pull perhaps a few hundredweight or at most 2 or 3 tons at a time, the broad horse-drawn barge could pull 60 tons.

above: A narrow-boat tied up alongside one of Titus Salt's mills on the Leeds & Liverpool Canal at the Saltaire World Heritage Site between Bradford and Shipley. Salt's huge woollen mill — combining the production facilities from five other mills on to this new site which also contained a model village for his workforce — was developed in 1851 and was designated a World Heritage on the 150th anniversary of its foundation.

Railways were still more than half a century in the future when the canal revolution started, so it was the canal system which made much of Britain's industrial revolution possible – providing a cheap and effective means of moving large quantities of materials and merchandise around the country, albeit rather slowly. But, then, it was a time when the pace of life was altogether more gentle than today, and 4 miles per hour for a laden 60 ton barge still represented a quicker means of bulk transportation than whatever the total time would have been for the equivalent number of cart journeys.

By the time the intense canal-building period drew to a close in the first quarter of the 19th century, Brindley's dream had largely been realised. It was possible to carry goods by canal and river navigation from London to Birmingham, Bristol, Liverpool, Manchester, Northampton, Lincoln, Bradford and Leeds, from Kings Lynn to Bedford and Cambridge, and countless other industrial and maritime centres.

The Scottish canal system was, for reasons of geography and cost, never connected to the southern network, but did link Glasgow to Edinburgh and Grangemouth across the centre of the country.

In the canal-building age, suggestions for canals came from some unexpected people. Writing in *A Tour Thro' the*

Whole ISLAND of GREAT BRITAIN in 1726, *Robinson Crusoe* author Daniel Defoe suggested a canal linking the Forth and the Clyde, writing

notwithstanding several circumstances which might obstruct it, and cause the workmen to fetch some winding turns out of the way, yet, that in the whole, a canal of about eight miles in length would fairly join the rivers, and make a clear navigation from the Irish to the German Sea.

He was no engineer. Forty years later John Smeaton developed a viable engineering solution to linking the two rivers, and work started in 1768. The canal, however, would not be 8 miles in length but 35. And rather than no locks as Defoe was suggesting, the project would require thirty-nine of them! It would take twenty-two years to build and cost several lives, and because of financing difficulties, would not open for traffic until 1790.

Scotland's other major canals – Telford's Caledonian and Rennie's Crinan Canal – both enjoyed continued success. The Forth & Clyde Canal was severed in the early 1960s to make way for road improvements, and the Union Canal abandoned a few years later. Returning them to use would take millions of pounds, and years of work, but the reinstatement of both, and the creation of the Falkirk Wheel, has given them a sustainable future as leisure routes.

above: Trencherfield Cotton Mill in Wigan – the third to be built on the site – had direct access to the Leeds & Liverpool Canal via its own short cutting. It was one of the last mills in Britain to be designed with canal transport as the primary means of receiving raw goods and dispatching manufactured cotton. It opened in 1908.

left: *Vienna*, a 'Josher' class cargo boat built in 1911 by Fellows, Morton & Clayton at their Saltley Dock works in Northwich. It is seen here at Cheddleton Flint Mill in Staffordshire in the 1990s. It is now known as *Verbena* and in the livery of South Midland Water Transport Limited.

The Anderton Canal Carrying Company was a short-lived transport enterprise set up in 1969 using a number of former Fellows, Morton & Clayton boats leased from the British Transport Commission — which had acquired FMC's assets in 1948. The Anderton Canal Carrying Company operated the boats for only three years before abandoning canal freight services. Built by Yarwoods of Northwich at a cost of £700 in 1936, *Shad*, had a load capacity of 25 tons. She worked between Wolverhampton, Ellesmere Port, Manchester and Nottingham, and is now preserved at the National Waterways Museum at Ellesmere Port.

In their heyday canals carried coal, iron, textiles, raw cotton and wool, and a hundred other commodities. Along their banks were built thousands of factories, many using the canals' water for their production processes as well as transportation.

To transport all those goods, companies built large fleets of cargo barges, some of the names being visible across the network.

One of the most widely seen in the heyday of the canals was Midland-based Fellows Morton & Clayton Ltd who became one of the largest and best known canal transportation companies in England. Their large fleet of boats travelled far and wide over the network. Their cargos were varied – indeed they advertised that they could transport any produce anywhere at an economic price.

Founded in West Bromwich in 1837 by James Fellows, and expanded after his death by his widow and his son Joshua, the company built up a fleet of more than fifty boats. Frederick

right: A sorry sight — the Rochdale Canal near Manchester city centre in 1968. Closed to traffic in 1952 — although not officially abandoned by Act of Parliament until 1965 — it would be fifty years before the full 53km of the canal was renovated and open to traffic from Manchester to Sowerby Bridge once more.

Morton joined as a partner in 1879, and Thomas Clayton's general cargo boats were absorbed into the business in the 1880s, the name of Fellows Morton & Clayton Ltd being adopted that same year. The fleet then comprised 11 steamers and approximately 112 horse-drawn 'butty boats'.

By the early years of the 20th century, the number of steamers had increased and these 'fly boats' – so named because of their speed – could complete a trip from London to Birmingham in less than two and a half days. The boats operated non-stop and the four-man crew would work in shifts throughout the journey, handling the boat and all the locks en route.

By 1935 the company was operating more than a hundred motor-powered boats, but just a few years later, in the face of intense competition from much faster services by road and rail, Fellows Morton & Clayton ceased trading in 1948. The name survives on a pub in Nottingham, and on numerous restored canal boats throughout the country.

By the 1950s, canals nationwide were falling out of use. Some remained busy, especially in the north of England, transporting huge quantities of coal to power stations, but the general cargo companies, gradually ceased trading.

Many of the waterways they had worked were simply abandoned, filling up with rubbish and losing vast quantities of water through decaying and leaking lock gates.

top left: Warehouses near Wigan Pier on the Leeds & Liverpool Canal, as they looked in 1970. The buildings, restored in 1986, now house The Orwell bars and restaurant – *see page 29.*

top right: *Rosemary*, a wide boat, lies sunk and covered in snow in the Rochdale Canal, winter 1968.

above: The remains of the Manchester Ship Canal Company barge *Cedar* lying partly submerged in the Shropshire Union Canal.

top: The Barton
Aqueduct carries the
Bridgewater Canal
over the River Irwell
and the Manchester
Ship Canal. Brindley's
1791 aqueduct was
replaced when the
Manchester Ship
Canal was built in the
1890s. The new
aqueduct opened in
1894 and is still in
use. It remains the
only swing aqueduct
in the world.

middle: The
Leamington Lift
Bridge over the Union
Canal in Edinburgh
was built by
Armstrong of
Newcastle in 1906
and was originally
sited closer to the
city centre. It was
moved to its present
position as part of
the Millennium
Project which
reopened both the
Union and Forth &
Clyde Canals. The
original hydraulics,
beyond repair after
fifty years of
inactivity, were
preserved and were
replaced with a
simpler mechanism.

right: A milepost on
the Chester and
Ellesmere Canal.

The area around the legendary Wigan Pier, for example, had become so derelict by the 1970s that the local council even considered demolishing the entire site. Comparing the scene on page 33 with the panoramic view on page 29 shows a remarkable rebirth. That same scale of transformation has been repeated on other canals throughout the country.

The restoration of the canal network nationwide over the past forty years has been an achievement which can only be described as miraculous – in many cases initiated by local bands of enthusiasts whose tireless efforts eventually paid off.

To see canals which have been closed for half a century once more open and busy is a remarkable testament to those who set the whole process in motion. Their restoration has initiated a long-overdue regeneration of the communities along their routes. Today a significant number of the former industrial complexes along the way have been turned into major tourist attractions, and several of those are featured elsewhere in this book.

above: Mariner's Canal, Salford Quays, part of the regeneration of Manchester Docks.

left: Two cranes stand as a reminder of Manchester Docks, looking somewhat out of place in the centre of a major modern develop-ment. The docks and the upper reaches of the Manchester Ship Canal were closed to commercial shipping in 1982 after eighty-eight years.

MINING

THE STEAM PUMPING ENGINE revolutionised mining. Mines could be dug deeper, and kept drier. In bringing about that revolution, one name stands above the others – Thomas Newcomen.

There are a number of surviving Newcomen-type engines today, perhaps the best known being Francis Thompson's 1791 engine preserved in the Science Museum in London. It was built for use at Oakerthorpe Colliery in Derbyshire, and the Science Museum claims it is the 'oldest Newcomen-type engine to survive complete and largely unaltered.' It is, however, not the oldest – that must surely go to the engine at Dartmouth which, according to researchers, dates from no later than 1725, just thirteen years after the first engine was built in 1712. The fact that the Dartmouth engine was rebuilt in the 1820s, however, gives validity to the Science Museum's claim.

Dartmouth's engine – acquired as part of the celebrations in 1964 of the 300th anniversary of Newcomen's birth – was one of two or perhaps three built for operation at Griff Colliery near Nuneaton in Warwickshire, at least one of which was operational by 1715. They were all in use a decade later, the second engine installed in 1719, the third – either a new build or a rebuild of one of the earlier two – in 1725. So the surviving engine was installed in the colliery between 1715 and 1725.

Newcomen had arranged a fee for the use of the engines, initially set at £7 per week in 1714, rising to £420 per year by 1725 – a significant sum in those days – for each mine drained. Clearly the commercial benefits more than out-weighed the cost.

By the late 1720s, the coal seams at Griff were virtually worked out and the two remaining engines were redundant, but here records as to what happened to them are unclear. According to some accounts, one of the engines was sold for use at Bedworth Colliery, south of Griff,

above: The plaque on the site of Newcomen's workshop near Bayard's Cove, Dartmouth, Devon.

below: Two views of the 1725 Newcomen Beam Engine, now at the Dartmouth Visitor Centre.

in 1731, the other to Oakthorpe Colliery near Measham in Leicestershire in 1734, a redundant brass cylinder from the one of the engines having reportedly already been sold to a colliery in Measham in 1729. However other sources state that one of the operational engines was sold to Measham in 1728.

The provenance of the Dartmouth engine is largely built on that premise. It is certainly of an early design, and fitted with a 22″ iron cylinder. This might suggest that it is a 1725 rebuild of either the first or second engines, with the redundant 16″ brass cylinder also being sold to Measham, perhaps for use on a smaller engine. Later engines were invariably larger. Without the invention of the steam pump, the whole story of mining might be very different indeed.

Mining once employed huge numbers of people in Britain, and their lives were both harsh and dangerous. Deaths in mining accidents a century ago – long before the days of health and safety considerations – were commonplace and numerous.

left: A group of visitors to the Big Pit, lamps checked and switched on, prepare to go underground.

By the time the widespread pit closures took place in the 1980s, they were thankfully fewer in numbers, but the cost in human lives of bringing coal to the surface has always been high.

Today, in a few carefully controlled situations, it is possible to go underground and get a sense of the conditions under which colliers worked. But in an inactive mine, the dangers they experienced can, thankfully, never really be replicated. It is still, however, a slightly unnerving experience going into a cage and being lowered down into the shaft, even if it is not a very deep one. The preserved shaft at Big Pit, the Welsh Mining Museum near Blaenafon, is just 100m deep, although the main workings were much deeper below ground.

For those who would wish to venture a little deeper, the National Coal Mining Museum for England at Overton near Wakefield in West Yorkshire has a shaft 140m deep. 100-140m is nothing when compared with the deepest mines in Wales and the North of England at more than 800m, but it is enough to give a real sense of the conditions below ground in which colliers worked day and night. Of course, deep underground in a pit, day and night were interchangeable – dark.

Mining rules and regulations are the same as they would have been in a working mine, so nothing with a battery in it can be taken into the cage. Watches, phones, cameras and battery-powered car key fobs all have to be left on the surface.

Then it is on with the collier's helmet, battery, light, and self-rescuer – a sort of gas mask – which would have been worn by every man setting off on his shift.

right: The Victorian lamp room at Beamish Colliery in Northumberland.

below: Also at Beamish, a replica of William Hetton's *Puffing Billy*, an early colliery locomotive.

below right: The 20th century lamp room at the Big Pit at the end of a shift. Electricity had replaced oil, and it was the responsibility of the lamp room staff to ensure all batteries were fully charged and checked before the lamps were issued to the colliers going on shift.

It takes about ninety seconds to reach the pit bottom, the cage descending at only half the speed it did when Big Pit was a working mine. In deep mines, a descent of eight to ten minutes was not unusual.

In the underground roadways, it is a little slippery underfoot at times, and hard hats are essential when walking along tunnels sometimes so low the colliers were bent almost double.

Visitors to the Lady Victoria Pit at Newtongrange get a rare opportunity to climb to the top of the headframe, and take a bird's eye view of the pityard. Sunk in the 1890s by the Lothian Coal Company and opened in 1895, the Lady Victoria Colliery is the best preserved group of Victorian mine buildings in Europe. The pit closed in 1981, and was one of the lucky few to be moth-balled. The good state of repair of its core late-Victorian buildings made it an ideal candidate site for the Scottish Mining Museum. The headframe and the Forth Bridge – visible from the top – were both built by William Arrol & Company of Glasgow. The railway bridge came first, opened in March 1890 – about the same time that work started sinking the Lady Victoria mine-shaft – and the 85-foot high frame was erected three years later.

More than 1,000 tons of navigation coal was brought out of the Big Pit each day at its peak – navigation coal being highly prized, as it was the ideal fuel for steamships and railway locomotives.

At one point along the way, visitors are told to switch off their cap-lights. Total darkness is not something we experience very often, but hundreds of feet underground, miners – or colliers as they preferred to be known – were totally dependent on their lamps. In the dark, with no points of reference, and only the sound of rushing water, and the reassuring sound of air being blown through the roadways, one could be anywhere facing in any directions, and with little chance of finding the way back along the tunnel. No collier would wish to be down there if he hadn't checked his batteries at the surface.

The three national mining museums in England, Scotland and Wales, are keeping alive memories of just how important coal was to the industrial progress of Britain.

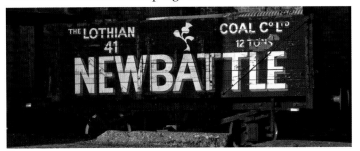

left: A pre-NCB 12 ton coal truck in the faded livery of The Lothian Coal Company's Newbattle Collieries, on display at Newtongrange.

The speed, and the completeness, with which just about every trace of the great heritage of coal mining has been wiped out is little short of remarkable.

In Scotland, for example, within five years of the end of the miners' strike in 1985, only one deep mine remained – the last of an undersea mining tradition which could trace its origins back to the 16th century, and Sir George Bruce's pioneering collieries at Culross on the River Forth. Elsewhere in Britain, the remaining few soldiered on. That lone Scottish deep mine – feeding the power station at Longannet – carried on for a further decade. Ironically, Scotland's first and last deep mines were just a few miles – but more than four centuries – apart, and both worked rich seams under the Forth. When that last mine went, a major disaster was narrowly averted. As *The Independent* reported on Saturday 30 March 2002,

Centuries of mining tradition came to an end when 77m litres (17m gallons) of water flooded the Longannet pit in Fife last Saturday after a dam separating old workings from new seams under the river Forth collapsed. If the breach had occurred 24 hours earlier, hundreds of miners would have drowned. The water poured into the five-mile mineshafts 1,970ft (600m) below ground in less than 10 minutes.

The fifteen men working underground at the time were in a part of the mine which escaped the flooding, and were all brought safely to the surface. Fear of inundation was ever-present in the mines which cut coal deep under the sea.

The industry once employed hundreds of thousands of people, and raised hundreds of millions of tons of the 'black diamonds' from deep below the surface. But away from the museums and the few surviving deep mines, there is little evidence of that history to be seen on the ground today.

Collieries and their smouldering spoil heaps could once be seen across the landscape of Britain's great coalfields – in Kent, the Midlands, Wales, Lancashire, Yorkshire and Scotland. But they have all been cleared, pithead buildings and washeries demolished, and in some cases, housing estates now completely cover former pit yards, the shafts beneath them carefully capped.

Just a century ago, Britain's collieries annually produced over 200,000,000 tons of various sorts of coal to heat our houses, power the country's mills and factories and fuel the railways and the great naval and merchant fleets of which Britain was rightly proud. Now we import coal.

But Britain mined many other minerals as well as coal – gold, silver, tin, copper and lead were also produced in commercial quantities. Most of those mines fared no better than the collieries, and the majority are now also abandoned.

Welsh and Scottish gold, highly treasured by anyone who has jewellery made out of it, has been mined for centuries, mines opening, closing and opening again as the price of these precious metals has fluctuated.

opposite top: The spoil heaps of Chisnall Hall Colliery, Coppull, Lancashire, photographed in the early 1970s. The site was cleared shortly afterwards.

opposite bottom: The 1902 concrete headframe of the Mary Colliery at Ballingry in Fife stands in the Lochore Meadows Country Park created out of the former pit site.

below left: Coal cutting head in the underground galleries at the Big Pit.

below: Pneumatic roof supports in the recreation of the coal face at Newtongrange.

The Towanroath Engine House, built on a precarious slope below the main mine buildings and opened in 1872, pumped water 200m from the Wheal Coates tin and copper mine near St Agnes in Cornwall. The mine opened in 1802 and operated for eighty-seven years. Briefly re-opened in 1911 it finally closed down in 1913. There were two other engine houses on the site, one operating the cage and giving access to and from the workings, the other powering an ore crusher.

opposite top: With thick Atlantic fog often gripping the hillside, this must have been an eerie and challenging place to work at times.

opposite bottom: In 1997, Wheal Coates was used as the setting for scenes in the John Hurt and Christian Bale film *All the Little Animals*, the site suitably dressed for the occasion with rusting trucks and other props to suggest an abandoned and dangerous ruin. The film, based on a Walker Hamilton novel, was released in 1998.

In Victorian times, parts of the north of Scotland even experienced a mini 'goldrush' as prospectors raced to try and make their fortunes. Shanty towns grew up to house them which would not have looked out of place in the Wild West.

While few traces remain of that goldrush, survivals of the Cornish tin and copper mining industry can be found dotted along the coast, and at several locations inland. Just as with coal, a number of them have been turned into fascinating museums exploring the history of the mines and their miners. The whole area was listed as a World Heritage Site in 2006, so important are the surviving remains of a once-vital industry.

It was not just coal mines where shafts were dug deep or out under the sea. Many Cornish mines tunnelled below the Atlantic Ocean, some shafts nearly 500m deep.

Although visitors are not taken that far underground, at both the Geevor Tin Mine Museum in Pendeen near Penzance, and Poldark Mine near Helston, underground tours are also part of the experience.

Like the Welsh gold mines, the commercial value of the huge deposits which still lie beneath Cornwall's landscape rise and fall in line with market forces.

It is said that the value of the ore beneath the World Heritage Site area is worth over £1.5 billion, but plans to start mining again – most notably at South Crofty Mine which was the last Cornish tin and copper mine to close in the late 1990s, and which had re-opened briefly in 2004 – have faltered

The mine's longer term future was put on hold in 2011 due to UNESCO's requirement for a comprehensive assess-

ment of the environmental impact of re-starting large scale mining in such an important heritage area. The mining company entered administration in 2013.

Most mines were wet, and over the centuries, ever more ingenious methods were evolved to drain them sufficiently to allow mining to continue. As soon as mines are closed and the pumps are switched off, water quickly fills the workings, making re-opening an expensive the difficult business.

On seeing the great beam engine which drained water from the lead mines at Wanlockhead in Dumfriesshire, Dorothy Wordsworth wrote in 1803 that

It heaved upwards once in half a minute with a slow motion, and seemed to rest to take breath at the bottom, its motion being accompanied with a sound between a groan and a 'jike'. There would have been something in this object very striking in any place, as it was impossible not to invest the machine with some faculty of intellect; it seemed to have made the first step from brute matter to purpose, showing its progress by great power. William made a remark to this effect, and Coleridge observed that it was like a giant with one idea.

In an observation on the life of the miners, she wrote that '*it is not common for people working in lead mines to be healthy*'. It most certainly wasn't.

The engine which the Wordsworths saw probably pre-dates the one on site today, – thought to have been installed a few years later, although no accurate records survive.

left: Colliers leaving a Wigan coal mine in the early years of the 20th century — still covered in the grime of a hard shift in the days before the introduction of pithead baths.

below: The miners' showers at Big Pit were built in 1939.

opposite top: Rusting ore trucks below the beam engine at Wanlockhead in Dumfriesshire.

opposite middle: Lead miners at Wanlockhead in the1890s.

Living and working conditions for the workforce in mines of all sorts remained surprisingly primitive well into the 20th century. The advent of electric lighting, and of electrically and hydraulically-powered mining equipment, together with improved drainage and ventilation, did make conditions underground a little less uncomfortable.

It was normal in Victorian and Edwardian times, for the working shift to start only when the miners had reached their actual place at work – and if that was 2,000 feet below ground and it took an hour to get there by cage and a long walk, so be it.

Their shift over, the long journey back to the surface was also unpaid, and the miners, filthy from their day's labour, would have to walk home, unwashed and still in their work clothes, to be scrubbed by their wives in tin baths in front of the fire.

Such 'luxuries' as pithead baths for the male workforce were not commonplace even in the inter-war years, and many northern collieries where women worked the coal screens, still had no washing facilities after the Second World War. A hard life indeed.

opposite bottom: An early beam engine was used to pump water out of the lead mines at Wanlockhead in Dumfriesshire. The first beam engine was erected on the site in 1745, but the present example dates from the 19th century. It was a water-bucket engine, operating round the clock, where the weight of water diverted from streams above the engine into a large wooden bucket operated the beam, enabling it to pump over 7000 litres of water an hour from the lead mine 30 metres below.

IRON & STEEL

THE EDWARDIANS LOVED POSTCARDS and had an insatiable appetite for subjects which reflected their lives and their work.

Thus we have historically invaluable and extensive series of views from the years before the Great War – many of them chromolithographed – celebrating the great industrial complexes which employed so many thousands of people. They survive in stark contrast to the bland postcards which are produced today, and in many cases illustrate sites which were demolished long ago.

One such site, the huge Summerlee Ironworks at Coatbridge, was demolished in the early 1930s after standing unused for years, but its industrial heritage is remembered today in *The Museum of Scottish Industrial Life* which now occupies part of the site.

Opened in 1836 by John Neilson, Summerlee used what was known as the 'hot blast' process, patented by James Beaumont Neilson, which recycled the hot gases produced during the smelting back through the furnaces, substantially improving their efficiency without increasing the consumption of coal.

Summerlee was one of Scotland's largest and most important ironworks, and Coatbridge was, for a time, known as the 'Iron Burgh'. As iron gave way to steel, however, in the latter part of the 19th Century, the ironworks went into decline and finally closed in 1926.

opposite page: The first cast iron bridge in the world crosses the Severn at Ironbridge in Shropshire. Built by Abraham Darby III, the grandson of his namesake who established the first iron foundry in Coalbrookdale, the bridge had no precedent, so constructing it was a significant engineering challenge. Each cast iron strut and beam was made to replicate existing patterns for wooden-arched bridges, and jointed and assembled much as a wooden bridge would have been. It opened in January 1781 six years after work on it started.

left: The huge Summerlee Ironworks in Coatbridge, from a 'Reliable Series' postcard c.1906.

above: The 0-4-0 tank engine *Lindsay* is the sole survivor of the many industrial steam locomotives built by the Wigan Coal and Iron Company at their Kirkless works. The company was owned by the Earl of Balcarres and Crawford, who also owned many of Wigan's largest coal mines. *Lindsay* – Lord Crawford's family name – was built in 1887 and worked at the Standish collieries. This photograph was taken at Steamtown, Carnforth (now closed) on the occasion of the locomotive's centenary in 1987.

above right: The huge Kirkless Ironworks of the Wigan Coal & Iron Company at Top Place, Wigan, adjacent to the Leeds & Liverpool Canal.

In recent years, the site of the ironworks has been partially excavated, and parts of the foundations of the blast furnaces can now be seen from an elevated viewing platform in the museum.

In South Wales, however, a much more complete understanding of the layout and processes of an ironworks can be gained.

Just under a mile from the Big Pit stand the ruins of Blaenafon Ironworks, work on the construction of which started in the late 18th century. The site is surrounded by the town of Blaenafon which grew up to house the men, women and children who mined the coal, iron ore and limestone, and who worked – often in unbearably unhealthy conditions – to turn those ores into iron.

The town did not exist before the industrial revolution, so just building a factory and housing was not enough. Chapels were built to look after the spiritual needs of the growing community, and a company shop to fill their material needs was built at the end of Engine Row, the first row of cottages to be completed around 1780. Today, that shop has been recreated and stocked with products typical of the time. At its peak, the coal and iron industries around Blaenafon employed over 13,000 people.

Together with parts of the town itself, the Big Pit, the Pontypool & Blaenavon Railway, and the Monmouthshire and Brecon Canal, the Ironworks became part of the Blaenavon World Heritage Site in 2000, a timely reminder of the importance those industries played in Britain's industrial past.

Only thirty years earlier, it had been suggested that the buildings be demolished and the whole site cleared – it was described as an eyesore and a public danger.

Stabilising and restoring the site – which closed in 1911 – will take many more years before CADW's vision for its future sustainability is fully realised. So what visitors see today is a vast 'work in progress'.

Blaenafon Ironworks makes no claim to have been the first of its kind – not even the first in Wales, Hirwaun and Dowlais Ironworks having predated it by a couple of decades. But what does make Blaenafon especially interesting is, in fact, an accident of its location and design. The site, while appearing very large, is in fact very compact – a feature dictated by its geography – and it is that compactness which was its eventual downfall.

As demand for iron grew, there was no opportunity for expansion, so the owners simply build a new complex at Forgeside on the other side of the valley near the Big Pit, leaving the old works to the ravages of time, nature, and a growing local demand for dressed stone. Effectively abandoned by the end of the 19th century, it was simply forgotten, leaving it today as the most original and complete example of an 18th and 19th century ironworks in Britain. Much of what visitors see today dates back nearly 200 years, and the most recent additions are dated to around 1860.

Dominating the site is the Balance Tower completed around 1839 and designed to use water power to raise raw materials such as coke, iron ore and limestone to the upper level of the works from where it was tipped into the tops of the blast furnaces.

Operating the Balance Tower was a skilled operation. The truck of raw material was loaded on to one side of the balance at the bottom level. On the opposite side of the wheel, and at

top: Blaenafon Ironworks looking from the foundries towards the remains of the blast furnaces.

above: On site is a model of how the ironworks looked in their heyday.

above: The 1839 Balance Tower, at the right of the picture, at Blaenafon was used to raise ore up to the top of the blast furnaces, left.

right: There were three blast furnaces at Blists Hill, opened in 1832, 1840 and 1844. The engine house dates from 1873. At Coalbrookdale, a water-powered blast furnace opened in 1658.

opposite page: Many of the Blaenafon workers lived on site, subject to the noise, heat and smoke of the working furnaces. Their simple cottages, and the community shop, have been restored to something like their appearance in the late 18th century.

the top, was a cast iron water tank. This was filled with water until its weight slightly exceeded the truck at the bottom. As the filled water tank descended, the truck of ore rose to the top where it was rolled out on to rails leading round to the furnace tops. The water tank was then emptied to lighten it, and raised back to the top so the process could be repeated once more.

At the upper level, hundreds of people worked breaking up the iron ore and roasting it in 'calcining ovens', while others converted the coal into coke. Many were women, and the Victorian writer Arthur Munby – who was fascinated by the lot of working women, noted in 1865 that the girls

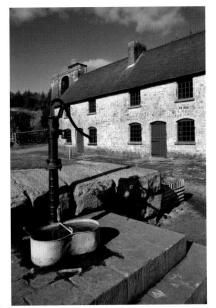

use heavy hammers ... lifting the hammer over their heads and bringing it down with manly skill and force. Fine strong girls they were ... they break stones thus from 6.00am to 6.00pm every day, ceasing only for breakfast and dinner, and earn six or seven shillings a week.

The work of feeding the furnaces was often undertaken by young boys, whose health suffered dreadfully from the effects of smoke and fume inhalation. Like their fathers, alongside whom they would work, their shifts lasted twelve hours, and they did one week of day and the next on nights. Appallingly – but these were the days long before Health & Safety – on 'changeover day' they worked the full twenty-four hours!

These furnaces never went out, so the raw materials were being tipped into searingly hot stacks, belching smoke and gases, and often propelling small clouds of burning gas up to the top.

The work was exhausting. The ore and fuel were taken out over bridges in two-wheeled barrows to be dropped into the raging fire below. Many of the boys – some as young as seven or eight years of age – were badly burned by the gases which were expelled through the furnace stacks at anything up to 300°C. They were also at risk of being overcome by carbon monoxide and other noxious gases belching out of the flames.

Each of the six furnaces had a casthouse or a foundry in front of it, the molten iron flowing straight from the furnaces into moulds either to make ingots of pig iron, or to be cast

above: An ornate cast-iron mangle in one of the casthouses at Blaenafon. Cast-iron goods were exported from British foundries all over the world.

into more ornate ironwork. On the casthouse and foundry floors, rusting cast iron, and equally rusting casting frames lie around awaiting restoration.

When the Lorn Furnace Company was established in 1753, it set about building an iron smelting works by the shores of Loch Etive, a sea loch on the west coast of Scotland. Its founders, Richard Ford & Company – also known as the Newland Company – were based in Barrow-in-Furness in present-day Cumbria.

Mid-18th century iron smelting required a prodigious amount of charcoal, which was hugely expensive to transport by either ship or road. Charcoal was bulky, so required large vessels. Thus transportation was a huge part of the manufacturing costs making it uneconomic to take the charcoal to the iron ore. So Richard Ford took the iron ore – in this case Cumbrian haematite – to wherever there was a ready supply of coppiced wood from which to make the charcoal.

The Benderloch area fitted the bill nicely – easy to get to by sea from Barrow-in Furness, with vast acreages of birch and oak forests, plentiful cheap local labour and, on the shores of Loch Etive there was a green-field site upon which to build the furnaces. So was established Bonawe Ironworks on the east side of the loch at Airds Bay just north of Taynuilt. Around it grew a thriving little industrial community.

From 1753 until the end of 1875, ships laden with iron ore sailed regularly from Barrow into the loch itself. And given the massive tidal range across the entrance to the loch, quite large

right: The remains of Bonawe Ironworks on the shores of Loch Etive are the most complete survival of a charcoal-fuelled ironworks in Britain. Bonawe finally closed in 1876, after 123 years. The furnace sits at the heart of the site surrounded by charcoal stores and a casting house. The remains are now in the care of Historic Scotland.

ships – in mid 18th-century terms – could make their way up to the quayside by the ironworks when the tide was high.

At the height of its operation, the works turned out more than two tons of pig-iron every working day, and employed around 600 people – most of them in coppicing and charcoal-making in the surrounding woodlands. During the Napoleonic War, the workforce was even employed casting canonballs for the British navy.

So important was the ironworks by the middle of the 19th century, that a military road was laid to Taynuilt and on to Bonawe as early as 1856. It would take twenty more years before a proper road was laid to the nearby port of Oban!

As the economics of scale encouraged the development of ever-bigger ships, access to the loch became more difficult, and using smaller vessels was, simply, impractical. The works eventually closed down in early 1876 and the site was abandoned. After the closure of Bonawe, the small ironworks at Backbarrow in Cumbria continued alone as the last iron-smelter still using charcoal as a fuel. Everyone else had progressed to coke, a much more efficient fuel.

Henry Bessemer's invention of a relatively low-cost process for converting iron into steel, pioneered in 1855,

above left: Two Edwardian views of the foundry at Vickers' Maxim Works in Barrow-in-Furness. Originally founded in 1871 as the Iron Shipbuilding Company by James Ramsden, the company changed its name to Barrow Shipbuilding before being taken over by Vickers in 1897.

above right: The huge 3-cylinder, 12,000ihp River Don Engine was built in 1905 to power Charles Cammell's armour plate rolling mill in his Grimesthorpe Works. The engine was one of four all built for the same purpose, and is the largest working steam engine in Europe. It could roll 3" thick armour plate.

right:
Middlesbrough's huge
Acklam Iron works,
from a tinted
postcard c.1905.

below left: A patent
1860s Nasmyth steam
hammer in Morton's
Ironworks at Blists
Hill, Ironbridge. It
was removed from
Thomas Walmsley &
Sons' Atlas Forge in
Bolton when that
closed in 1973, the
last company in the
world producing
wrought iron.

below right: A Rigby's
Patent steam
hammer in use in
Wigan. c.1890.

opposite: Four
Edwardian postcards
from a series
celebrating
Sheffield's cutlery
makers. From the
top, they depict
metal buffers,
cutlers at work,
etching cutlery, and
knife grinders.

initiated a downturn in the fortune of the cast-iron industry. Steel was a much more durable and versatile metal, and although its manufacture had been understood for centuries it was, before Bessemer, a difficult material to produce in quantity, and thus expensive.

What Bessemer discovered was that the oxygen necessary to convert iron into mild steel – hitherto introduced by adding iron oxide to the pig iron – could actually be achieved by blasting air directly into the molten metal. Not only did this remove the unwanted carbon from the iron, but the conversion

into mild steel could be completed on a large and commercially viable scale in just a few minutes.

Despite his obvious success, steel-makers were reluctant to adopt Bessemer's idea, and he eventually felt driven to build his own steel works in Sheffield. When he demonstrated that he was able to produce steel at a substantially lower price than traditional methods – 25 tons at a time – Bessemer's process quickly became widely accepted. Within a relatively few years, Sheffield had developed into Britain's steel capital, with a growing number of plants.

Output grew exponentially as demand for the material grew, and the city's population grew from around 70,000 in the 1850s to nearly 500,000 by 1910 and, with the development of stainless steel by Henry Brearley in 1912, that demand increased further. One of Bessemer's converters has been preserved in Sheffield's Kelham Island Museum.

Demand, however, called for faster processes, and Bessemer's process was replaced first by Open-Hearth steelmaking, and then by the Electric Arc process which is still used today.

Templeborough Steelworks in Rotherham opened in 1892 and eventually had fourteen open-hearth furnaces, their chimneys known locally as the 'Fourteen Sisters'. They were replaced by six Electric Arc furnaces in the early 1960s, the last open-hearth furnace being tapped for the final time on 23 December 1964, and the sixth and last electric arc furnace being switched on two months later. 'E' furnace remains in place today, the works now open as Magna Science Adventure Centre.

The financial collapse of the early 1920s was a major setback – steel-making plants closed and many thousands of men were laid off – but by the time H. V. Morton visited the town in 1927 while writing his book *The Call of*

right: A Bessemer
crucible about to be
emptied, photo-
graphed at Leeds
Steel Works in
Hunslett around 1910.

below right: The last
electric arc furnace
in the former
Templeborough Steel
Works — now the
Magna Science
Centre — in
Rotherham. Today,
in what they call
'The Big Melt',
pyrotechnics and
sound effects
recreate the steel-
making process.

below: A boiler
explosion at Leeds
Steel Works on 26
August 1913 caused
nine men to lose
their lives.

bottom: A furnace
explosion at Ardsley
on 28 August 1908
cost five lives.
Gothard of Barnsley
published both
postcards.

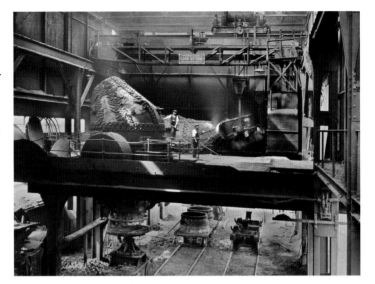

58

left: The 25-ton Bessemer Converter — now preserved at Sheffield's Kelham Island Museum — was used by the British Steel Corporation until 1974 and is one of a very few still to survive.

below: Built in 1851 by Murdock, Aitken, & Company of Glasgow for the Lillieshall Company's Priorslee Ironworks, the great beam blowing engines, David and Sampson, operated full time until 1900, and as standby engines until decommissioned in 1952. They blew air into four coke-fired blast furnaces. The engines are now at Blists Hill.

England, business was picking up again. The city which greeted him was enjoying a welcome recovery, about which he wrote with his usual eloquence –

As one by one the black chimneys of Sheffield come to life, as one by one the orange flames of the blast furnaces return to the night, the spirit of this grim city rises, and her men are encouraged.

She is a city of machines that bend steel, that bore holes in steel, that shave steel in long, curling lengths as easily and smoothly as a knife cuts bread.

She is perhaps the most spectacular expression in England of man's control over the rough materials of his existence.

Iron and steel formed the backbone of Britain's industrial development in the 19th and 20th centuries. Just about everything we use today is either made of steel, or manufactured using machines made of steel. Without steel, our modern world just could not exist. Hundreds of different types of steel, each made with specific characteristics, are now produced.

Because of the size of iron and steel works, their significance is woefully under-represented in preserved and accessible sites and museums, but those places which do tell their story are well worth a visit.

BRITAIN'S RAILWAYS

UNTIL DR BEECHING, and in the era before widespread car ownership, railways were Britain's transport arteries; they were a socially and economically essential part of the passenger transport system.

They were the 'common carrier' charged with transporting freight and livestock for anyone to just about anywhere. They pretty much covered the country linking small towns with big cities, and linking small towns with even smaller towns on lines which had never made any profit for their Victorian investors. Inevitably, thousands of miles and hundreds of stations were axed, as the railways effectively conceded defeat to the motor car and the articulated truck.

The railway age made fortunes and lost fortunes. Those who invested in the major routes anticipated that they would reap rewards beyond their dreams. A few did, many didn't.

Every new railway company required an Act of Parliament to approve its plans, keeping Parliament busy, but meaning that the development times of new routes were inevitably quite long.

In total, over 1,000 railway companies were set up, some of them to build and operate major routes, others hoping to find fortunes in short local branch lines.

To create all those lines required civil engineering projects on a major scale, and to operate them, locomotive and rolling stock builders sprang up all over the country.

opposite: Manchester Central Station was opened in 1880 by the Cheshire Lines Committee – a partnership between the Great Northern Railway, the Midland Railway, and the Manchester, Sheffield & Lincolnshire Railway – offering a rival route south. It closed in 1969 and quickly fell into disrepair. At the time this photograph was taken in 1972, it had just been sold to NCP to be made into a car park. However in 1986 it reopened as the GMEX Exhibition Centre, and is now known once again as Manchester Central.

above: Aboyne Station in Aberdeenshire as it looked in 1972. It is now a retail centre.

left: The elaborate arcading of Wemyss Bay Station, Ayrshire, which was opened by the Caledonian Railway in 1903.

top: W. H. Smith's railway map, 1880s.

middle: Weighing scales at Haverthwaite Station, Cumbria.

above: Awaiting restoration, a wooden-bodied third-class LNER carriage at Carnforth, 1970s.

From the simple beginnings in the 1830s, right up to – and beyond – the end of the 19th century, the pace of development was little short of frantic.

A look at any railway map in the closing years of the 19th century would show just how ambitious – and ultimately doomed to failure – many of the railway-building projects were, but in building them the landscape of Britain was changed forever.

W. H. Smith's railway map from the 1880s – which cost a substantial two shillings – shows that by then it was possible to travel from just about anywhere in the country to just about anywhere else. And to aid passengers in planning their journeys, complex timetables were widely available, and regularly re-printed as the network expanded.

From as early as 1839, travellers could consult George Bradshaw's pioneering book *Bradshaw's Railway Time Tables and Assistant to Railway Travelling*. Each subsequent year that book got bigger – its name shortened to *Bradshaw's Railway Companion* – and sold in vast numbers.

More than any other form of transport throughout the Victorian and Edwardian eras, the railways opened up the country for both commerce and pleasure, and introduced the population to the idea of long distance travel. Before the railways, few people ever travelled more than day's walk or horse-ride from where they lived.

But as with every new innovation, the railways did not meet with universal approval. Landowners – Queen Victoria amongst them – who were determined the lines would not cross their lands or pass within earshot of their stately homes and castles, imposed tortuous detours on some of the planned routes. Many of them were more than happy to sell the coal which fuelled the locomotives, and travel by rail when needs must, but they did not wish to see or hear them at other times.

To some, it was the speed of railway travel – several times faster than coach travel – which caused concern. No lesser figure than the Duke of Wellington is on record in 1827 as saying '*I see no reason to suppose that these machines will force themselves into general use.*' Others, like John Ruskin, believed railways would destroy the beauty of the landscape forever – a strange opinion to us today who think that the plumes of smoke and steam from a heritage train making its way through a pleasant

valley is something both beautiful and filled with nostalgia.

The Whig politician Thomas Creevey found the experience of his first railway journey – travelling at a reputed 23mph – terrifying, writing

The quickest motion is to me frightful; it is really flying, and it is impossible to divest yourself of the notion of instant death to all upon the least accident happening. It gave me a headache which has not left me yet.

The dangers of this new fast form of transport became apparent very early. In September 1830, on the opening day of the Liverpool to Manchester Railway, Creevey's political colleague William Huskisson became the first person to be killed by a passenger train. Huskisson was travelling as a

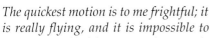

above left: Rowley Station, a late-Edwardian NER branch line station, rebuilt at Beamish.

top: Rowley Station ticket office at Beamish is furnished with equipment typical of the period before the Great War.

above: Carnforth Station in Lancashire, from a tinted Edwardian postcard.

left: The ex-Great Western Railway 4-6-0 *Hinton Manor*, built in Swindon in 1939, standing at Hampton Loade Station on the Severn Valley Railway.

above: The Leaderfoot Viaduct in the Scottish Borders carried the Berwickshire Railway over the River Tweed. Built in 1865, it connected Reston on the east coast North British Railway with St Boswell's on the Waverley Line.

above right: Seen from Conwy Castle, Robert Stephenson's 1849 bridge over the River Conway runs alongside Telford's 1826 suspension bridge. This is the only surviving example of Stephenson's tubular bridges since the Britannia Bridge was lost to fire in 1970.

passenger with the Duke of Wellington, but disembarked at Parkside Station near Newton-le-Willows, to talk to acquaintances. He walked across the line in front of an on-coming train and was killed when he fell under the wheels of the most famous of all the early locomotives, Stephenson's *Rocket*. He was not the first fatality of the railway age, however.

Several navvies had lost their lives in the construction of the first railway lines – and countless more would die building the rest of the network.

Huskisson was not even the first person to be killed by a moving train. During a blizzard in December 1821, a carpenter by the name of David Brook was killed by a locomotive while walking home along the track of the Middleton Railway in Yorkshire and, in 1827, local papers in Eaglescliffe on Teesside had reported the death of a blind beggar struck by a locomotive.

As the 19th century drew to a close, an estimated 20,000 route miles had been constructed and were operational, served by 7,500 stations.

By the outbreak of the Great War, amalgamations, takeovers and closures had reduced the number of companies from the original 1,000 which had been granted parliamentary approval, to around 150, and the mileage had

already been reduced to around 16,000. By the 1920s, the network was dominated by the 'big four' railway companies, and they in turn were reduced to just one on nationalization.

After Dr Richard Beeching wielded his axe in the 1960s, total track mileage was cut to less than 12,000, the 7,500 stations open in 1900 reduced to fewer than 3,000.

It would, therefore, be a significant mistake to put all the closures down to Dr Beeching. Many lines had slipped into bankruptcy long before the end of the 19th century, and additional routes were abandoned when the Big Four groupings were created in 1923. More were closed by British Railways when the network was nationalised after the Second World War, but the geography of the Beeching cuts was especially hard-hitting, based as it was on passenger numbers rather than on social need. Thus, a significant number of little-used lines were axed, in many cases whether or not there were alternative means of transport for those affected. Even many large towns were cut off from the system leaving their residents wholly dependent on cars or infrequent bus services.

Central to Dr Beeching's original brief from government had been to make the railways profitable – something they had not been since before the Second World War. Nationalisation

above left: An unusual view of the most recognisable railway bridge in the world – the Forth Bridge – photographed from a boat passing beneath it. Opened in 1889, it still carries Scotland's main east coast railway line today.

above: Riding on the footplate of Lydham Manor on the Dartmouth Steam Railway in Devon. Lydham Manor was built at Swindon for British Railways in 1950, and is one of nine survivors of a class of 30 built between 1938 and 1950.

above: The London Brighton & South Coast Railway locomotive *Gladstone*, restored in 1927.

right: The Tay Bridge c.1904, with an 8-coach northbound train standing at Wormit Station.

below right: Wormit Station buildings today, part of Bo'ness Station on the Bo'ness & Kinneil Railway.

opposite top: The London & North Western Railway's 1873 *Hardwicke*, at York's National Railway Museum.

opposite middle: The 1842 former Haymarket train shed, rebuilt at Bo'ness Station on the Bo'ness & Kinneil Railway.

opposite bottom: Haverthwaite Station platform in the late 1970s. The line had been re-opened to Lakeside in 1973.

had not achieved it, and Beeching's first round of cuts achieved little benefit.

Getting rid of steam, considered inefficient and expensive to staff and maintain – with the perceived benefit of creating a cleaner railway – was not resisted at all by the general public. Diesel railcars were considered modern, and initially at least they certainly were cleaner. Nostalgia for steam was still a thing of the future.

Scrapyards all over the country became the graveyards of steam, and initially only a few people lamented their disappearance.

Fast forward nearly half a century from the Beeching closures, and the long-term outcome of the good doctor's plans has certainly not entirely been what he anticipated. Heritage railways abound, new and imaginative uses have been found for abandoned stations, new stations are being constructed – and even some abandoned lines are being relaid.

New steam locomotives have been commissioned to help meet our growing nostalgic attachment to the leviathans which Beeching sought to remove forever from British metals.

On several heritage lines, buildings which would otherwise have been demolished, have been carefully rebuilt. At Beamish Open Air Museum in Northumberland, the former Rowley Station buildings stand just a few yards from the rebuilt Carr House East Signal Box.

At Bo'ness on the Scottish Railway Preservation Society's Bo'ness & Kinneil Railway, the cast iron train shed from Edinburgh's Haymarket Station – dating from 1842 – stands adjacent to Wormit Station buildings which once stood at the south end of the Tay Bridge.

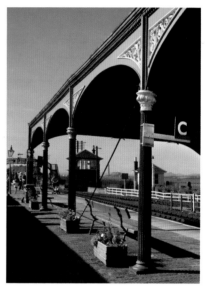

The signal box just a few yards from the station was originally Garnqueen South Junction Box, built by the Caledonian Railway, while the footbridge adjacent to it originally stood at the Highland Railway's Murthly Station north of Perth. Further up the heritage line at Birkhill, visitors can see the rebuilt Monifieth Station which once stood on the main line east of Dundee. The surviving building dates in part from 1838.

Preservation of historic locomotives and rolling stock started long before the widespread withdrawal of steam and the ensuing route closures of the 1960s.

The London, Brighton & South Coast Railway's 0-4-2 passenger engine *Gladstone* carries a 1977 plaque commemorating fifty years since the locomotive was preserved for posterity. The B1 Class locomotive *Gladstone* was built in Brighton in 1882,

The 26-lever frame in Carr House East Signal Box, rebuilt near Rowley Station at Beamish. This array was operational c.1950, when the signal box stood near Consett in County Durham. Levers 6, 7, 12, 18, 21 and 26 (in white) were unused.

below: Cranmore Signal Box on the East Somerset Railway. The signal box, built in 1904, was stripped of all its equipment when the line closed in 1968, and for many years served as a gallery for the railway's then owner, artist David Shepherd. Since 2000, work has been on-going to restore the box, and it now contains a 26-lever signal frame and ancillary equipment. Originally broad gauge, the East Somerset Railway opened in 1855. The 1901-built Hudswell Clarke 0-6-0 in GWR livery, carrying No.813, approaching the platform has just run round the train. Built for work in Port Talbot Docks, the locomotive was bought by the GWR in 1923 and sold on in 1924. No.813 is now based on the Severn Valley Railway.

designed by William Stroudley and withdrawn from service in 1926 after travelling more than 1.3 million miles.

Gladstone is now displayed in the National Railway Museum, which opened in the former York North Sheds in 1975.

In his 1928 book *The Call of England*, Henry Vollans Morton – H. V. Morton as he always styled himself – described a visit to the North Sheds at the peak of their activity.

Trains drop and pick up locomotives at York. No.4 shed running department is a great parade ground of green giants. A turntable occupies its centre, and round this in a circle, set regularly like the spokes of a wheel, are dozens of big engines, steam up – 'just like human beings', as Bill says – waiting to run on the turntable and so out on the night's job. Behind No.4

above: A poster for Glasgow's steam-powered and cable-driven underground system, opened in 1896. The subway was re-engineered as an electric railway in 1935.

left: *Mallard*, Sir Nigel Gresley's famous A4 'Pacific' locomotive – still holder of the world steam speed record, and now preserved at the National Railway Museum – was built in Doncaster in 1938. Mallard is seen past the front of Sir William Stanier's rival LMS Coronation Class 'Pacific' *Duchess of Hamilton*, built at Crewe, also in 1938. *Duchess of Hamilton* was originally built as a streamlined locomotive, but was rebuilt to semi-streamlined standard with smoke deflectors after the Second World War, and given the British Railways number 46229. The locomotive was re-streamlined at Tyseley in 2009, her LMS number – 6229 – restored.

shed is No.3, full of less spectacular goods locos, and No.1, where the small tanks and the humdrum engines stand. Sometimes an antediluvian of no known category puffs into No.1 shed with a brass hump like a fireman's helmet behind its tall smoke-stack. Even the natives of No.1 shed let off a little steam at him.

Predating *Thomas the Tank Engine*'s talking locomotives by nearly two decades, Morton's account of the York sheds had the LNER locomotives poking fun at each others as early as 1928.

'Hullo,' they hiss, 'who left the museum door open?'
'And how did you leave Mr. Stephenson, dearie?'
All the embittered locals hiss with unkind laughter.
But the green Olympians of No.4, their flanks shining, their piston-rods slightly green with new oil, the steam rising truly and gradually in their gauges, their boiler tubes clean as a whistle, their coal-tubs full, are superior to this tittle-tattle. They are removed from the ribaldry of the lesser sheds, isolated in their magnificence like Guards officers on parade.

To see the sheds today crammed with the finest collection of preserved railway locomotives in the world, would surely have pleased Morton considerably.

He also visited the city's original railway station just a few steps from the present one. In 2013, the old York & North Midland Railway station buildings were adapted and given a new lease of life as York City Council offices.

SHIPPING & SHIPBUILDING

IN JUST A FEW DECADES, Britain has gone from being the world's leading shipbuilding nation, to being a country where the only significant vessels being built in British yards are naval. When Britannia ruled the waves, a huge proportion of the world's naval and merchant tonnage was launched from British yards – and many more were built in British-owned yards throughout the Empire.

A century ago, shipyards on the Clyde, Tyne, Tees, Mersey and Wear all had full order books, and huge workforces.

In the early 1960s, the Caledonian Steam Packet Company, which operated pleasure steamers on the Clyde, sold its passengers a little booklet, priced 6d (2.5p), which identified everything they would see on their trip 'doon the watter'. In addition to castles, distilleries and other points of interest, the booklet still pointed out the locations of no fewer than thirty shipyards.

The mighty *Queen Elizabeth 2*, arguably the most beautiful trans-Atlantic liner even built, was launched into the river from John Brown's yard in 1967, but of Brown's yard, Napier's, Inglis' and many other great shipbuilding names, hardly a trace remains. Only a restored but solitary Titan crane marks where John Brown's launched more than three hundred ships, including the RMS *Lusitania*, RMS *Queen Mary*, RMS *Queen Elizabeth*, HMS *Hood*, and the QE2.

Of the thirty yards listed in 1961, only those at Govan and Scotstoun – formerly Fairfields and Yarrows respectively and now owned by BAE Systems Surface Ships building naval vessels – and Ferguson Shipbuilders of Port Glasgow, still launch ships on to the river. Today Ferguson's output seems restricted to small ferries for Caledonian MacBrayne, and when they launched CalMac's MV *Hallaig* in 2012, it was the first vessel to be entirely built on the river in five years. At the time of writing, the future of the former Yarrow & Company yard at Scotstoun is in doubt as BAE seeks to rationalise and modernise its warship facilities.

In his book *In Search of Scotland* published in 1929, H. V. Morton suggested to his readers, after he had watched a ship being launched into the Clyde, that 'A new keel is like a large

above: The 1961 brochure produced by the Caledonian Steam Packet Company for passengers on their Clyde pleasure steamers. On the cover is the turbine steamer *Queen Mary II*, built as TSS *Queen Mary* – originally fitted with twin funnels – at Denny's yard in Dumbarton in 1933. She was renamed *Queen Mary II* from 1935 until 1976 and is now in Tilbury Docks, her future uncertain.

opposite page: HMS *Trincomalee*, restored and moored in Hartlepool, was built of teak in Bombay, now Mumbai, in 1817. Britain's oak forests had already been virtually exhausted.

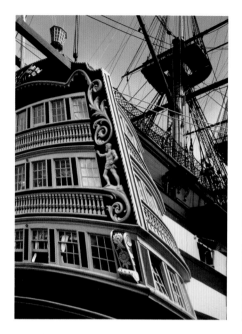

glass of whisky on a cold day: it warms the very core of Glasgow's heart.'

The ship he saw launched was, most likely, the 8,139grt SS *Yoma,* launched at the Dumbarton yard of William Denny & Brothers on 2 September 1928. *Yoma* was destined for the Far-Eastern route from Glasgow to Rangoon

(Yangon) in Burma. She operated between the two ports for twelve years until being commandeered for war service in 1940. She was torpedoed and sunk on June 17 1943.

All that remains of the Denny yard today is the 100m long ship hull test tank, installed in 1881, and used for over a hundred years to test the efficiency of hull designs.

Some of the great yards on the Clyde, the Tyne and elsewhere, are derelict wastelands, and have been for years, their equipment gone, their buildings demolished, their slipways and fitting-out basins filled in. Of many other yards, hardly a trace remains as waterside sites have been redeveloped for residential and leisure uses.

The Pointhouse yard on the Clyde, where A. & J. Inglis built so many fine ships, is now the site of Glasgow's new

transport museum designed by Zaha Hadid – with the 1896-built steel-hulled sailing ship *Glenlee* moored alongside. *Glenlee*, which spent her later life as a Portugese naval training ship and renamed *Galatea* before being abandoned in Seville, has been restored, not to her 1896 condition, but to something more akin to her appearance in the 1920s. Her true heritage and national importance as one of the last-surviving Clyde-built sailing ships was recognised only in 1990, and over the past twenty-five years, her rebirth has been a remarkable and very convincing achievement.

Perhaps against the odds, quite a number of other nationally important ships have been restored and given a new lease of life as tourist attractions – amongst them Brunel's SS *Great Britain*, HMY *Britannia*, HMS *Trincomalee* and HMS *Warrior* – both rebuilt at Hartlepool – and, of course, HMS *Victory*.

How much of what we see is original is, in some cases, a question best not asked as several of them were little more than hulks when their visionary rescuers thought restoration might be possible.

Victorian naval engineering was developing at a considerable pace when *Warrior* entered service in 1861, and despite her many innovative features, even she became virtually obsolete very quickly, being withdrawn from 'first line' service after only ten years, and from active service in 1883. From 1902 she was a stationary depot ship at Portsmouth for twenty-two years and, after five years of

opposite top left: The steel-hulled barque SV Glenlee, built at Anderson Rodger's Bay Shipyard in Port Glasgow in 1896, is one of only five surviving Clyde-built sailing ships.

opposite top right: Captain Scott's vessel RRS Discovery was built at the Dundee Shipbuilders Company's Panmure yard, and launched in 1901.

opposite bottom left: HMS Warrior was built at Blackwall on the Thames in the yard of the Thames Ironworks & Shipbuilding Company and commissioned in 1861.

opposite bottom right: The ketch Irene was built by F. J. Carver & Sons in Bridgwater, Somerset Now restored, she is available for sail training and charter.

left: A replica of HMS Warrior's horizontal trunk engine. The connecting rod can be seen entering the trunk at the top of the picture. The real engine operated at 56rpm, while the replica turns at a much more sedate 2.5rpm.

75

above: Metal workers pose with their steel plate rolling mill at a Sunderland shipyard, in the 1890s.

above right: The RMS *Caronia* under construction in John Brown's shipyard on the Clyde, 1904.

below: The bridge telegraph on the Dunedin-built TSS *Earnslaw* was made by Chadburn's of Liverpool, considered to be the best in the world. Launched in 1912, the coal-fired twin-screw steamer celebrated her centenary recently, and still sails the waters of Lake Wakatipu in South Island New Zealand. Chadburn telegraphs were exported to shipbuilders all over the world.

disuse, she was stripped of all her equipment and fittings in 1929, and relegated to the role of fuelling hulk at Llanion Cove, Pembroke Dock, becoming known as *Oil Fuel Hulk C77* – a somewhat ignominious end to the career of such a pioneering vessel. There she stayed for almost fifty years until rescued in 1978 and towed 800 miles to Hartlepool for restoration.

When it comes to preserved and restored historic ships, the former frigate HMS *Trincomalee*, reclassified as a spar-decked corvette after her rebuild in 1845, is one of the most important – and the oldest warship still afloat anywhere in Europe. She originally cost £30,323.00 to build in 1817. Her rebuild completed in 2005 cost more than £10.5M.

HMS *Trincomalee* was built in Mumbai, then known as Bombay – and that is a key factor in her survival for almost two centuries, for she was built of Indian teak, a wood well known for its longevity in water.

Building a wooden-hulled man-of-war could require up to 2,000 trees, and the great naval shipbuilding effort of the 17th and 18th centuries had de-forested huge tracts of Britain. The teak forests inland from Mumbai were vast, acquisition of the timber was cheap, and the city's East India Company shipyard had an exemplary reputation. Many of Britain's warships were built there in the early 19th century.

While many preserved vessels are in drydocks or moored to quaysides, *Irene* – the last tall ship to be built in the Somerset port of Bridgewater – is still sailing, restored in the 1980s and rebuilt again after a near-disastrous fire in 2003.

British shipbuilding was once the envy of the world – the terms 'Clyde-built' and 'Tyne-built' by-words for quality – but, sadly, that is just a memory.

Sunderland was once described as the 'largest ship-building town in the world', and the industry employed many thousands of workers throughout the 19th and 20th

left: The complex guidance systems in the control room of the submarine HMS *Alliance*. Now exhibited at the Submarine Museum in Gosport, she was built by Vickers in Barrow, laid down in March 1945, but not commissioned until 1947. The submarine is displayed as she looked after her rebuild in 1958, with enclosed conning tower and upgraded equipment.

centuries. The town's last yard, however, closed in 1988 amidst huge local protests.

The last ship to be built on the Tyne left the Swan Hunter yard in 2006, ending a century and a half of shipbuilding on the river. RFA *Lyme Bay* left incomplete, being towed round Britain to Govan for fitting out. A sad, bizarre end to a way of life and a rich heritage.

Over its long existence, Swan Hunter built more than 1,500 ships and employed tens of thousands of people. When *Lyme Bay* left the yard, fewer than 300 were still employed.

The docks at which the great cargo ships loaded and unloaded their cargoes have been similarly closed down and redeveloped, and nowadays seeing a merchant ship on the upper reaches of the Clyde, or sailing past Liverpool's Three Graces is anything but a common sight.

Manchester Docks have completely gone having operated for little more than eighty years, a casualty of economic considerations which made only the largest of ships profitable.

above: The launch of HMS *Lord Nelson* from Palmers' yard in Jarrow in 1905. One of the largest ships built at the yard, HMS *Lord Nelson* cost £1.6M to build — about £350M at today's prices and thus a lot cheaper in real terms than our sophisticated warships these days. She served in the navy for only eleven years from 1908 until 1919.

above: The engine room of the Royal Yacht, HMY *Britannia*, built at John Brown's Clydebank yard, 1953.

above right: The bridge on HMY *Britannia*.

below: HMY *Britannia*, moored at Leith, her beautiful profile diminished by the visitor facilities aft.

When the Manchester Ship Canal was being built, its planners thought they had future-proofed it, but the maximum size of vessels able to negotiate the waterway – 12,500grt – seems so small by comparison with today's huge container vessels. Ships today unload at Eastham at the Mersey end of the canal, the canal itself host only to the occasional boatload of tourists.

Going back a century and a half, Britain's maritime trade was in the ascendancy, its docks a constant bustle, as goods of every type were imported and exported.

Henry Mayhew in his 1860s work *London Labour and the London Poor* offered his readers a vivid description of London's docks.

left: The 1960-built, 1,323grt, MV *Yewkyle* at Leith Docks in 1973, with the 1962-built 10,449grt, MV *Irish Plane* behind. *Yewkyle* had five owners and five names in forty-three years. MV *Irish Plane* sailed for Irish Shipping Ltd until 1976.

As you enter the dock the sight of the forest of masts in the distance, and the tall chimneys vomiting clouds of black smoke, and the many coloured flags flying in the air, has a most peculiar effect; while the sheds with the monster wheels arching through the roofs look like the paddle-boxes of huge steamers. Along the quay you see, now men with their faces blue with indigo, and now gaugers, with their long brass-tipped rule dripping with spirit from the cask they have been probing. Then come a group of flaxen-haired sailors chattering German; and next a black sailor, with a cotton handkerchief twisted turban-like round his head. Presently a blue-smocked butcher, with fresh meat and a bunch of cabbages on a tray on his shoulder; and shortly afterwards, a mate, with green paroquets in a wooden cage. Here you will see sitting on a bench a sorrowful-looking woman, with new bright cooking tins at her feet, telling

below left: Manchester Docks, January 1968, from a crane on No.9 Dock. Over 5,000 vessels used the port in 1968 carrying over 15 million tons of cargo. The docks, now known as Salford Quays, have been redeveloped for housing, offices and leisure.

below: Manchester Liners' 8,734grt 1964-built MV *Manchester City* at Manchester's No.8 Dock in 1968.

you she is an emigrant preparing for her voyage. As you pass along the quay the air is pungent with tobacco; on that it overpowers you with the fumes of rum; then you are nearly sickened with the stench of hides, and huge bins of horns; and shortly afterwards the atmosphere is fragrant with coffee and spice. Nearly everywhere you meet stacks of cork, or else yellow bins of sulphur, or lead-coloured copper ore. As you enter this warehouse, the floor is sticky, as if it had been newly tarred, with the sugar that has leaked through the casks.

Leo H. Grindon, in his 1882 *History of Lancashire* offered his readers an equally vivid picture of Liverpool's docks.

Merchant-men predominate, but, in addition, there are almost invariably two or three of the superb steamers which have their proper home upon the Atlantic, and in a few hours will be away. The great Companies whose names are so familiar, the Cunard, the Allan, the White Star, the Inman, and five or six others, despatch between them no fewer than ten of these splendid vessels every week, and fortnightly, two extra, the same number arriving at similar intervals.

Besides these are the South Americans, the steamers to the East and West Indies, China, Japan, and the West Coast of Africa, the weight varying from 1500 to 4000 tons, fifty-four going out every month, and as many coming in. The total number of ships and steamers actually in the docks, Birkenhead included, on the 6th of December, 1880, was 438.

London Docks, he went on to tell his readers, may have been larger, more famous, and covered more area, but in October 1880 alone Liverpool had imported no less than 167,400 barrels of apples from North America.

While many of the major docks are gone, their roles taken over by a few vast container ports, a considerable number of smaller docks survive, some turned into marinas – like Watchet in Somerset and Bo'ness on the Forth – with others like Goole and Falmouth still shipping cargo in and out,

Ports such as Aberdeen have been given a new lease of life by the oil industry, and along the south coast, Dover, Southampton, Portsmouth and Plymouth amongst others, depend on our enthusiasm for taking our cars to Europe, and also on visiting cruise liners. At the time of writing, Leith's attempt to turn itself into a cruise-ship destination has not been successful.

The industrial remains of others, now scheduled as ancient monuments, have themselves become tourist attractions.

Porthgain in Pembrokeshire once exported slate and when that ceased, a brickworks was established. Towards the end of the 19th century the port shipped crushed stone for road-making, and the huge brick-built hoppers for the stone still dominate the harbour.

At Beadnell on the Northumberland coast, late 18th century lime kilns still stand testament to the little port's industrial past.

The quicklime produced in kilns such as these had a very short life when exposed to the atmosphere, so it was important that it was transported away from the kilns to the cement works as soon as possible after the process of making it was complete. Harbourside locations were ideal for this.

opposite top: Porthgain Harbour in Pembrokeshire, seen over the top of the 19th century stone hoppers. The export of crushed stone from the port continued from the late 1890s until the mid 1930s.

opposite middle: The mouth of one of Porthgain's hoppers on the harbourside.

opposite bottom: Beadnell's late 18th century limekilns are now restored and used as fishermen's stores.

below left: The overgrown ruins of Lord Elgin's lime kilns adjacent to Charlestown Harbour on the Firth of Forth.

below: Working inside the Charlestown lime kilns must have been an extremely unpleasant experience.

above: The former Mersey Bar Lightship is now a café/bar on Liverpool's waterfront.

Much larger are the Charlestown lime kilns on the Firth of Forth, established by Lord Elgin in 1750. They were being expanded in number and output when the 18th century traveller Thomas Pennant visited in 1772. He described them as 'the greatest perhaps in the universe, placed amidst inexhaustible beds of limestone, and near immense seams of coal.'

The kilns were so vast that it took two weeks for the limestone to be reduced to quicklime and fall to the bottom of the furnaces to be raked out. Again, the closeness of the harbour was a key to commercial success – as was the ready supply of cheap fuel mined locally from the Fife coalfields.

Luckily, significant examples of early mercantile architecture have also survived – although often by accident rather than design.

Jesse Hartley's Albert Dock in Liverpool is one such gem – the first-ever custom-built dock complex in the world, still with us simply because when it had outlived its usefulness by the 1920s, its demolition was considered uneconomic. Long before then, however, the increasing size of merchant vessels had limited use of the Albert Dock to those few vessels which displaced less than 1,000 tons.

below: A small cargo vessel being unloaded at Glasson Dock on the Lune estuary in Lancashire, early 1980s. The port still ships coal out and imports fertilisers.

below right: The MV *Alnlam* at Goole in 1973. Since the closure of Manchester, Goole in Yorkshire, 72km from the sea, is now Britain's most inland working dock.

Hartley's vision was ground-breaking. In the Albert Dock he created an efficient system for the unloading and storage of imported goods with tall warehouse blocks lining the quaysides, each with integral cranes – a total of 21 – and cranes on the opposite sides of the buildings for moving cargo out on to carts and railway wagons.

The docks were completed in 1847 at a cost approaching three quarters of a million pounds and opened by Prince Albert.

What made it ground-breaking was not only its security, but the fact that it was the first fire-proof dock complex in the

world, built entirely from brick, stone and cast iron, with no wood in it at all. From an historical point of view today, its importance is that the buildings and most of the original features are still intact, albeit that the cranes were converted to hydraulic power in the 1880s.

Now fully restored, the warehouses host residential property, shopping arcades, bars and restaurants, the award-winning Merseyside Maritime Museum, and Tate Liverpool. Along with the rest of Liverpool's historic waterfront, the Albert Dock is listed as a UNESCO World Heritage Site.

Some of the features in the Albert Dock were pioneered in London's St Katherine's Dock, opened in 1828. Like its Liverpool counterpart, St Katherine's was also a casualty of increasing ship size. While the Albert Dock remained undamaged, however, large parts of St Katherine's were destroyed in the Second World War.

Elsewhere around the country, important relics of Britain's maritime past can also be found – and are listed in the gazetteer – but Britain's days of ruling the waves are now well in the past.

top: A solitary cargo ship passes Port Glasgow on the Clyde.

The Anderston Crane – a Glasgow landmark.

above: The River Mersey at Liverpool, not a ship in sight.

left: Liverpool's Albert Dock, now redeveloped for shopping and leisure.

TRADE & MANUFACTURE

BRITISH GOODS WERE EXPORTED to just about every country in the world. In Victorian and Edwardian times British factories had full order books, and 'British Made' meant 'well made'.

opposite: Bottle ovens were once a common feature of the industrial landscape around Stoke-on-Trent. Now just a few remain. These two are at the Gladstone Pottery Museum.

As manufacturing on an industrial scale has diminished since the 1960s – and as competing countries have caught up – many of the huge factories which turned out everything from tableware to locomotives have ceased operation and been demolished.

Other facilities have simply been replaced as manufacturing techniques have changed and the requirements of a modern production line have become ever more sophisticated.

Those which have survived, however, have fascinating stories to tell of industries which once employed thousands of men and women up and down the country.

below: The18th century Cheddleton Flint Mill played a key role in the development of fine tableware in Georgian times. The mill's two flint kilns can be seen in the lower photograph.

They remain either because there was no economic need to demolish them, or because the processes they carried out changed little over the years. Many, now open as museums, are priceless windows through which to access history.

The many great bottle ovens which once dominated the landscape around Stoke-on-Trent are now represented by just a few. Those in the Gladstone Pottery Museum are part of a complex which tells the story of the Potteries – everything from tableware to Thomas Crapper's famous toilets.

The area around Stoke developed as a centre for pottery due to the vast supplies of good quality clay, and a ready local supply of coal, but in the 17th and early 18th centuries, the ceramics they produced were relatively crude.

White tableware was created by covering the red clayware with a heavy white glaze, but as Georgian society increased in sophistication, and demanded finer wares, a process which had been

below: Rubislaw Granite Quarry near Aberdeen was the source of much of the stone for the city's Victorian and Edwardian buildings. A postcard c.1905.

bottom left: Stone has been quarried from the island of Portland for centuries, and the quarries are still operational today.

bottom right: The tiny west coast Scottish island of Easdale was once at the heart of the country's slate industry. Centuries of tide-worn slate waste litters the shoreline.

known since the middle of the previous century became essential to the ceramics industry.

Finely ground flint when added to clay, it was discovered, not only whitened the resulting fired pottery – requiring a lighter coating of glaze – but also enabled the potters to produce finer and lighter wares such as Josiah Wedgwood's popular 'Creamware'.

Credit for this innovation is usually given to John Astbury who employed it in the early 1720s, but the processes involved in creating ground flint – a very fine powder which was too easily inhaled – were very injurious to the health of those who milled it. A Staffordshire miller, Thomas Benson, developed a process for grinding the flint wet, thus making the process much safer.

Flint mills using Benson's process were opened up all around the Potteries, the finest survival being at Cheddleton on the banks of the Caldon Canal.

There are two mills on the Cheddleton site, both breast-shot watermills, the older of the two having been converted in the mid 18th century from a long-established corn mill. What remains today is largely of late 18th century origin, comprising the specially constructed north mill, two large kilns to 'roast' the flint, and a drying kiln to convert the wet slurry into a fine powder.

Cheddleton's position by the canalside was crucial to its operation. Flint and coal both arrived by barge and were loaded directly into the kilns at the canal bank. Flint, when heated became easier to grind to the fine powder necessary for use in ceramics.

The millstones needed to grind flint – even burned flint – had to be made of a much harder stone than would have been needed in the mill's earlier time grinding corn. The preferred stone was chert, a very dense silica-rich stone not unlike flint itself, but much harder.

The later development of the china clay industry – much of the raw material for which was mined in Cornwall – would render many flint mills largely obsolete, but several carried on well into the middle of the last century, grinding flint, animal bones and other materials. Ground bone and bone ash were, after all, key ingredients in the manufacture of that very English – and much sought after – material, bone china, initially developed by Thomas Frye in London in the mid-18th century, and refined by Josiah Spode. Bone china could be manufactured into tableware which was finer, stronger, whiter and, above all, translucent.

Increasing demand for all sorts of manufactured goods inevitably meant the development of larger production facilities – factories and mills – and the migration of large numbers of people into towns and cities seeking employment in these new large 'manufactories'.

The growing wealth of industrialists in the 19th century in turn led to the construction not just of great houses for themselves and their families, but bold statements of civic wealth – grandiose town halls, museums and galleries – and town centres where they could spend their money in theatres, department stores, and elsewhere.

above: An ancient paved road across Blackstone Edge in north-east Lancashire. Often referred to as a Roman road, this early cart road more likely dates from the late 17th or early 18th century.

Bolton Town Hall, an impressive statement of civic pride and industrial power. Like Leeds, Manchester, Stockport and elsewhere in the north of England, Bolton's wealth came from textiles – it was one of Lancashire's most productive cotton towns. The town hall, completed in 1873 after seven years of construction, and set in a wide open space, was a testament to anyone who visited the town that Bolton was a modern and successful community.

87

above: Postcards, clockwise from the top: Workers leaving the Singer factory in Clydebank, c.1904; Netmaking at Joseph Gundry & Co, Bridport, Dorset, 1903; Westinghouse Works, Trafford Park, Manchester, c.1904; Workers leaving Huntley & Palmer's biscuit factory, Reading, 1907.

below: An Edwardian enamel Raphael Tuck advertisement, displayed at Beamish.

Britain's rapidly expanding manufacturing base led to the development, in the closing years of the 19th century, of an entirely new concept – the industrial estate.

The establishment of one of the first was triggered by the opening of the Manchester Ship Canal in 1894. Trafford Park, once a heavily-wooded deer park, fronted on to the canal, and was an ideal location for this new development. First to set up on the site was the Westinghouse Corporation, and by the early 20th century, their huge factory complex alone employed more than 12,000 people.

The Edwardians celebrated their diverse industries in countless postcards, many of which were never posted, but simply collected for their enduring social interest.

The mass production of photographic postcards came about as a result of the invention of the half-tone screen in 1888, and a significant improvement in the quality of chromo-lithographic printing.

The half-tone screen broke the fine detail of the photograph up into small dots, enabling printing plates to be made which could reproduce the tonal detail of the original picture.

The versatility of the half-tone screen had, in turn, led to the introduction of photographically illustrated newspapers before the end of the 19th century, while rotary presses greatly speeded up the newspaper print process.

Until offset-lithography replaced 'hot metal' printing in the newspaper industry – a changeover which started at the beginning of the century and accelerated in the 1950s – the production of a newspaper had changed little since the introduction of the rotary printing press. Due to the cost of replacing presses, many local newspapers had still not changed over to lithography in the 1970s.

top left: Running a rotary newspaper press, *Evening Post & Chronicle*, Wigan 1972.

top right: Sign outside Robert Smail's printing works, Innerleithen.

above: Checking the flong, newspaper printing works, 1972.

It was a lengthy process preparing a page for printing on a rotary press. First the type was set in lead, half tone printing blocks were created for photographs, and the whole page was set up in a frame known as a 'chase'. From that, a papier-maché 'flong' or mould was made – the process had been invented in France in the late 1820s – which was then used to cast a curved lead plate which was fixed to the rotary printing press, inked up and printed.

To experience the range of skills involved in early printing processes, a visit to the John Jarrold Printing Museum in Norwich or the National Trust for Scotland's Robert Smail's Printing Works in Innerleithen in the Scottish Borders – where there are regular printing demonstrations and hands-on opportunities to do a little typesetting – is highly recommended. In the last forty years, the computer has rendered so many of these skills largely obsolete.

The production of food and drink has also changed out of all recognition with industrialisation, with local bakeries

right: Adding hops to the boiling wort in the copper at the Three Daggers Micro-Brewery, Eddington, Wiltshire, 2014.

below: Hop pickers and a Kent Malt House, around 1905, as seen on Edwardian postcards.

below right: The Victorian maltings at Snape in Suffolk, as they looked in 1980. They now house shops and galleries.

right: Malt whisky casks outside the Glenturret Distillery in Perthshire, 2009. Like many distilleries, Glenturret now offers visitor tours.

left: Open from 1899 until 1983, Dallas Dhu Distillery, Forres, is now in the care of Historic Scotland. Visitors see the malt barn, kiln, mash house, tun room, still house and bonded warehouses. The distillery closed due to a shortage of water after a long drought in 1983.

giving way to large factories and blander products. The development and refinement of tin-plate led to a revolution in the preserving and canning of produce, and the improving transport links led to the speedier movement of produce around the country.

In the drinks industry, many small breweries and maltings which had continued virtually unchanged for a century closed down in the 1970s and 1980s as larger-scale breweries owned by multi-nationals rendered them uneconomic.

But the 'real ale' movement brought about a change in drinking habits for many and in the 21st century, with some products, their appeal is now very much based on them still

below left: Tossing barley on the malt-house floor at Tullibardine Distillery, Perthshire, July 1969.

below right: Weighing barrels of newly distilled Tullibardine Single Malt prior to them going into the bonded store, July 1969. A bottle of this vintage – which would have spent more than thirty years in the cask and is now very rare – would today cost upwards of £250.

being made by traditional means. The rising popularity of these ales is reflected in the growing number of breweries and micro-breweries where the beers and ales are still produced in a way, and on a scale, our Victorian ancestors would have recognised.

Likewise the finest malt whiskies are still distilled by traditional means and on a relatively modest scale – and many breweries, cider-houses and distilleries today welcome visitors who would like to know more about how their favourite tipple is made.

above right: Women packing Sunlight Soap at Port Sunlight, Cheshire, c.1906.

above: On the shelves in the recreation of an Edwardian corner shop at the end of the preserved terrace of houses in Susannah Place, Sydney, Australia, are many of the British-manufactured goods which would have been familiar to local residents – including Sunlight Soap of course, Fry's Cocoa, Tate & Lyle's Golden Syrup and Robertson's Marmalade, all sharing space with locally produced goods.

Some might regret that many places are kept going largely as tourist attractions, their commercial viability depending as much on visitors' entrance fees as the prices paid for their products, but at least they are still operating – keeping history alive for us all to enjoy.

While the industrialisation of Britain was dependent upon the ready availability of power sources – water, wind and coal have been explored earlier in this book – it was equally dependent upon an efficient transport infrastructure. The canals, railways and developing national road system were crucial. The 18th century saw major improvements in roads and the early years of the 19th century saw development of well-surfaced trunk roads thanks to the pioneering work of John Loudon Macadam.

The country's engineering prowess led to the development of ever more powerful and efficient systems for moving raw materials and manufactured goods in and out of foundries, shipyards and locomotive works.

The iron and steel industry had made possible the mass production of rails for railways and tramways. Suburban railways and trams – first horse-drawn, then steam-hauled and eventually driven by electricity – were key to moving large numbers of people to and from the manufacturing facilities. By the beginning of the 20th century, factories – hitherto built beside canals – were being sited where there was immediate access to the railway network, shortening distribution times considerably.

While the vast majority of tramcars were disposed of in the 1950s, a notable exception being on Blackpool's Golden Mile, a few were preserved in transport museums, and over the past half a century and more, many others have been lovingly restored and can be seen doing what they were designed to do at Beamish, Coalbrookedale, and the National Tramway Museum at Crich in Derbyshire – which now has more than sixty preserved trams.

The tramcar's demise came about as a result of our growing love affair with the motor car, while the decision to

below left: Wigan operated steam trams in the late 19th century. The double-decked bogie cars were hauled by locomotives made by William Wilkinson of Pemberton, Wigan, and by Kitson's at their Airedale Works in Leeds.

below: Stirling's trams were always horse-drawn, the system operating from 1874 until 1920.

Sunderland's No.16 tramcar, built in Preston in 1900 by Dick, Kerr & Co, was initially a single-deck vehicle. It was converted to a double-decker in 1920, and operated until the Sunderland tram system was dismantled in 1954. After spending many years as a garden shed, the tram was rescued and rebuilt at Beamish.

right: The Leyland/DAF production line in Lancashire, in 1990. American-owned since 1993, Leyland Trucks Ltd is now the UK's largest lorry manufacturer.

below: Argyll Motors of Alexandria, gearbox shop (left) and chassis works (right), 1906.

bottom: A 1964-built half-scale replica of a London Metropolitan tram, on the Seaton Tramway in Devon.

move more and more freight from rail to road – something which has since increased relentlessly – was directly responsible for the closure of great tracts of the railway network in the 1960s.

The ascendancy of the motor car, however, continued at an increasing pace – between the wars, and especially after the Second World War – and, from small beginnings, the motor industry became a major national employer.

left: A 40 year old RAF Vickers VC-10 over the North Sea, in 2010.

below left: The 1963 Hillman Imp was the first and only mass-market car ever to be built in Scotland.

Hand-built car makers were eventually overwhelmed by large-scale manufacturers – Austin, Ford and others – whose brands soon dominated the market.

below: Charles S. Rolls flew non-stop across the Channel and back on 2 June 1910.

Catalogues from early motor shows list over a hundred companies all vying for their share of the growing market but, with the exception of a very few famous names, they have all gone.

bottom: Claude Graham-White with his biplane, Blackpool Air Show, 1910.

Even many of those well-known marques which still flourished long after the Second World War – Austin, Jowett, Morris, Riley, Rover, Standard, Triumph, Wolseley and others – have disappeared as our preference for European and Far-Eastern cars has grown.

bottom left: A 1929 Rolls Royce Phantom 2 Barker Boat-Tail, one of 31 Rolls Royces built for the Maharajah of Baroda.

One brand which is still very much with us – albeit now German-owned – is Rolls Royce which was established in May 1904, when Henry Royce, already a successful engineer, joined forces with Charles Rolls, owner of one of Britain's first car dealerships.

But Charles Rolls was not just a pioneer in the world of motor cars. He was also a pioneer aviator, and a record-

top: Avro Lancaster KB976 as it looked in the early 1980s. The aircraft was severely damaged in a hanger roof collapse a decade later and is now in pieces and dispersed.

above: The BAC TSR-2 tactical strike aircraft was cancelled in the 1960s due to spiralling costs. Two survive – this one at the Imperial War Museum site at Duxford, the other at RAF Cosford.

holder as the first man to complete a non-stop flight from Dover, across the Channel to Sangette in France, without landing, completing the journey in ninety minutes, only to be killed just a month later when his plane crashed.

As with so many other technological developments, Britain was at the forefront of the early aviation industry, developing many iconic aircraft which made their manufacturers world famous. Into the 1950s, such names as Armstrong Whitworth, Avro, Blackburn, Bristol, De Haviland, English Electric, Fairey, Gloster, Handley Page, Hawker, Supermarine, Vickers and others were familiar to plane-spotters of all ages.

Aircraft development had been driven by the outbreak of the Great War, introducing fighter planes and bombers by Airco De Haviland, Beardmore, Bristol, The Royal Aircraft Factory, Sopwith, Vickers and others to the skies over Europe.

The Vickers Vimy bomber lived on long after the end of the war, with civilian variants also being developed.

At the start of the Second World War, the RAF was still flying bi-planes – the Gloster Gladiator had only been introduced in 1934 – alongside more 'modern' aircraft such as Hawker's Hurricane and Supermarine's Spitfire. By the war's end, they were flying jets – the Gloster Meteor setting new standards for speed and versatility.

The post-war years saw huge leaps in aircraft technology, with the maiden flight of the world's first passenger jet – the De Havilland Comet – in 1949, and just twenty years later, the first flight of the supersonic Anglo-French Concorde.

Most of the long-established aircraft company names disappeared when they were absorbed into two groupings in the 1960s, at which time the industry directly employed over a quarter of a million people. Today, just over half that number are directly employed in aircraft projects including the Airbus family of passenger jets and the Euro-fighter Typhoon.

above: Waiting for take-off – the author in the cockpit of an RAF Hercules C130J.

left: The cramped flight deck of the only Avro Vulcan still flying – XH558 – now restored and operated by the *Vulcan to the Sky Trust*. The Vulcan was one of the three 'V Bombers' built for the RAF, the others being the Handley Page Victor and the Vickers Valiant.

middle: XH558 being prepared for flight.

bottom: The pilot's view of a Vickers VC-10 tanker during the mid-air refuelling of a Hercules C130J transport plane over the North Sea. The VC-10 was produced in relatively small numbers, and flown as a passenger aircraft by BOAC from 1962 until 1981. The last RAF VC-10 tanker flew in September 2013. Several examples are preserved – at Duxford, Brooklands, Newquay and Brungtingthorpe.

TEXTILE INDUSTRIES

BRITAIN'S BREAD HANGS ON LANCASHIRE'S THREAD was a popular saying in the 19th century, so important was cotton to the country's economic success. But it was not just cotton – wool, silk, jute and hemp all played their role in the textile industry.

For two centuries, in the damp air of cotton mills across the country, tens of thousands of people worked to spin hundreds of millions of miles of yarn, and weave millions of miles of cotton cloth. Throughout the 19th century, and well into the 20th, the industry just grew and grew.

But while output got larger and larger throughout the 1800s, the size of the workforce did not expand proportionately. It was mechanisation, rather than an increase in workforce, which fuelled the huge expansion in output – with power looms, the weaver went from being a self-employed craftsman at the end of the 18th century, to little more than someone who tended the machine a century later!

As Leo Grindon wrote in his 1881 *Lancashire: Brief Historical and Descriptive notes*, 'The Lancashire Cotton towns owe their existence essentially to the magic touch of modern mechanical art'. Where one weaver had worked one loom in the closing years of the 18th century, one weaver was in control of six or more looms by 1900, and by the time Wigan's last weaving shed closed in the late 1980s, just a handful of weavers were overseeing the smooth operation of an entire weaving shed.

top: A winch over the saw bed at Stott Park Bobbin Mills in Cumbria.

above: Raw jute at Dundee's restored Verdant Jute Works.

left: A tinted Edwardian postcard, showing workers in the Warping Room of an unidentified mill.

opposite page: Titus Salt's 1853 wool and alpaca mill, at Saltaire near Shipley, was powered by the waters of the River Aire.

99

To some in the 1830s factories were the peak of man's achievement, while to others they were the 'dark satanic mills' of which William Blake had so eloquently written. James Philip Kay, in his 1832 book *The Moral and Physical Condition of the Working Classes Employed in the Cotton Manufacture in Manchester*, wrote of mill work as being

The dull routine of ceaseless drudgery, in which the same mechanical process is incessantly repeated, resembles the torment of Sisyphus – the toil, like the rock, recoils

perpetually on the wearied operative. The mind gathers neither stores nor strength from the constant extension and retraction of the same muscles. The intellect slumbers in supine inertness. To condemn man to such severity of toil is, in some measure, to cultivate in him the habits of an animal.

top: At New Lanark mills, demonstrations of cotton spinning are part of the visitor experience.

above: Wooden bobbins, used throughout the textiles industry, were made in small mills built near ready sources of easily-coppiced wood. These were photographed at Stott Park Mill, Cumbria. In the days before steam power, bobbin mills were driven by fast running water, and worked constantly to supply the many spinning mills across Britain.

In the *Manchester & Salford Advertiser* of 29 November 1832, one Parson Bull described mill-owners as being

A race whose wisdom consists in that cunning which enables them to devise the cheapest possible means for getting out of the youngest possible workers the greatest amount of labour, in the shortest possible amount of time, for the least possible amount of wages.

Others – many fewer – disagreed, but one who did was Andrew Ure who, in his 1835 book *The Philosophy of Manufacture* claimed the mill-worker had an easy life, writing

In the factory, every member of the loom is so adjusted that the driving force leaves the attendant nearly nothing to do, certainly no muscular fatigue to sustain, while it produces for him good, unfailing wages, besides a healthy workshop gratis: whereas the non-factory weaver, having everything to execute by muscular exertion, finds the labour irksome.

Spinning and weaving sheds were dangerous places, the noise was deafening and the recurrence of serious injury was commonplace. 'In the rooms and sheds devoted to weaving,' wrote Grindon, 'the rattle of the machinery forbids even conversation, except when the voice is adjusted to it.' In fact,

the women learned to lip read, and could thus communicate across the entire shed. Perhaps surprisingly, he added that 'In the quieter parts, the girls show their contentedness, not unfrequently, by singing'.

The 19th century workforce was swelled by large numbers of children. From the 1878 Factory Act, the minimum working age was raised to ten, and Grindon, ever keen to put what we today would call 'a positive spin' on things, noted that

it is a blessing alike to them and their parents, since if not there, the children now earning their bread would be idling, and probably in mischief.

Fifty years later, H. V. Morton visited a Manchester mill and, echoing Grindon, found mill girls singing *Madame Butterfly*, and was told by one of the girls that 'We produced *La Boheme* last winter'.

top: Quarry Bank Mill in Styal, Cheshire.

middle Workers' cottages, Styal.

above: The small coop store in the Styal workers' village.

top left: Stanley Mills, a late 18th and early 19th century cotton mill right in the heart of wool country.

above left: Saltaire Mill is six storeys high and almost 180m long.

The mill itself was, he said, standing 'by the same stream that gave it power in the day's of Arkwright's water-frame'. In the weaving shed itself, he described a scene of 'organised pandemonium' and, again like Grindon, noticed that the girls were all lip-reading.

They were weaving artificial silk and cotton. Above certain looms danced a series of perforated bath mats. They told me that these were Jacquard looms. Every time the bath mats did their little Charleston steps a bit more 'art' silk pattern arrived on someone's pyjamas.

above: An early wooden hand-loom displayed at the Verdant Works.

The name of Richard Arkwright is usually associated with Lancashire, and the great cotton mills which dotted the north-west of England, but the best preserved Arkwright mill in the world is not in any of the expected places – Preston, Bolton or Wigan – but in the Perthshire village of Stanley by the banks of the River Tay.

Walking through the almost-deserted mills today – deserted, that is, except for visitors and Historic Scotland staff – the 229-year history of the place is brought back to life by displays and the recorded spoken memories of those who worked there.

below: The interior of the re-created workers' shop at New Lanark.

Most of the equipment has long gone – sold off when the mills closed in 1989 – but the voices and the sounds which echo across the empty spinning and weaving floors speak of the importance of the mill's contribution to local life and employment.

below right: The New Lanark Mills seen from above, built adjacent to the Clyde. When first built, New Lanark's mills were entirely water-powered.

It was a group of Perth merchants who joined forces with Arkwright to establish Stanley Mills – Arkwright providing some of the money, and a lot of technical expertise. But why Perth? Perthshire already had a skilled textile workforce

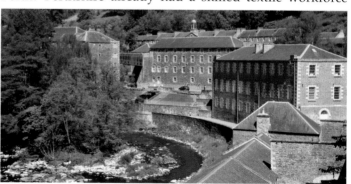

before 1784, in the form of a tradition for producing linen – local farmers grew the flax, and local spinners and weavers did the rest. The Tay is Britain's fastest-flowing river, and at Stanley it is flowing at its fastest – and in those early years of the Industrial Revolution, water-power was without doubt the most efficient way of driving machinery.

Those advantages – water power and a skilled workforce – outweighed the remoteness of the location, and its distance from the great west coast ports where the bulk of cotton was imported.

The same was true of New Lanark, now a World Heritage Site centred on the cotton mills and village where Robert Owen's pioneering model community was developed in the 18th century. Owen's ideas for establishing a humane working and living environment for his cotton workers was in stark contrast to the image of the 'dark satanic mills' already being developed elsewhere. He sought to establish a healthier and more civilized work/life balance, educating his workers' children – as well as using them as cheap labour – and providing decent housing. That the mill and village complex he developed has survived is remarkable, and its restoration in recent years makes for a truly fascinating visit.

In Thomas Pennant's late 18th century account of his tour of Scotland, he mentioned the manufacture of three quarters of a million yards annually of 'Osnaburgs' – brown linen – in Arbroath, and the later establishment of the linen production

top left: A volunteer demonstrates jute weaving on a small loom at the Verdant Works in Dundee.

top right: Katie Campbell at work on her Harris Tweed loom on the Isle of Harris in 2006. All Harris Tweed is still made by individual weavers on hand-looms.

above: The Verdant Works yard.

right: As the first stage of the carding process, blended wool is fed into the Scribbler where the fibres are straightened out between sets of spiked rollers before being fed into the carding machine by a swivelling 'Scotch Feed'. Coldharbour Mill, Devon.

below: The Carding Room in a Lancashire cotton mill, from an Edwardian tinted postcard. Rows of ring spinning machines can be seen beyond.

above: Spinning jute in one of Dundee's many mills – a postcard c.1906. At the time the industry employed thousands of workers, many of them women, as in cotton mills.

on an even greater scale in Dundee, where it largely replaced the long-established woollen industry.

By 1773, the year after Pennant's visit, almost four and a half million yards of the material had been woven in Dundee's mills. 'These are shipped for London, Newcastle, Leith, Burrowstoness [Bo'ness today], and Glasgow,' he wrote, 'from whence they are sent to the West Indies and America, for the clothing of slaves.'

By the end of the 19th century, however, jute production had replaced brown linen, and over 200,000 tons of raw jute – in the form of a million tightly packed 4-hundredweight bales – were being shipped from India to Dundee every year, to feed the city's hundred or so jute mills.

Until the 1950s, demand for jute was huge, used to make sackcloth, ropes and twines, carpets, linoleum, tents, and sailcloth to name but a few. By then, however, the glory days of jute had almost gone and the city's last four mills, Constable Works, Taybank Works, Manhattan Works and the Victoria Spinning Works closed in the 1990s. The industry's importance to the city is celebrated in the Verdant Works, a former jute mill now established as a museum.

left: A Scottish hand-loom weaver at work in his home workshop, from a postcard c.1905.

below: The Weaving Shed, Harle Syke Mill, Burnley, c.1907, showing ten of the mill's 1,700 looms, and just seven of its workforce.

Despite the scale of its jute, linen and cotton industries, Scotland is best known for its tweeds and its knitwear. The word 'tweed' is said to derive from a mis-spelling of the Scots word 'tweel' – an alternative for 'twill' – by a London hatter, and it is not apparently recorded anywhere as the name of a fabric before 1847.

Tweed manufacture expanded rapidly in the second half of the 19th century, and the mills – concentrated around the Border towns of Hawick, Galashiels, Selkirk, and Innerleithen – employed thousands of people, and became a hugely important export for Scotland. Sadly, many of those mills have long gone, priced out of the market by foreign imports and the growth in the popularity of synthetic fabrics. Others, however, thrive, and some of them offer fascinating mill tours allowing visitors to see the whole process of fabric-making from the raw wools to the finished clothing.

Whereas the manufacture of tweeds developed on an industrial scale in the Lothians and the Borders, Harris Tweed retains the most traditional approach to manufacturing. The Harris Tweed orb symbol is known worldwide and was one of the earliest trademarks to become widely recognised as a symbol of quality and craftsmanship after the passing of the 1905 Trade Marks Act and the establishment of the Harris Tweed Association in Stornoway in 1909.

Since 1911, all genuine Harris Tweed has been identified by the orb. To carry the label, the tweed originally had to be woven from locally-dyed and hand-spun yarns, but that changed in

above: Four Wigan mill girls pose for the camera in their work clothes, at the studio of Hill & Sons in the late 1890s. Working in the mill gave these girls their first real sense of freedom, and they developed enduring friendships.

top: Inside the last cotton weaving shed in Wigan — operated by Dorma Ltd at Eckersley's Mill — seen here in 1987 shortly before it closed. The noise inside the shed was deafening — and the 180 looms were controlled by just ten weavers. In Edwardian times, that many looms would have required 60 weavers and apprentices.

middle: A weaver at work in Arthur Dickson & Company's Wilderhaugh Street Tweed Mill, Galashiels, photographed in 1968. Most of Dickson's output at the time was produced for Munrospun Ltd., whose wool and knitware mill was in Restalrig, Edinburgh. Wilderhaugh Street Mill has since been demolished.

right and below: Some of the hand-looms used by Cartwright & Sheldon at Macclesfield's Paradise Silk Mill date from the 1860s. The mill ceased production in 1981.

1934 when mill-spun yarns were allowed for the first time – but only if they had been dyed and spun in mills on the islands.

Today there are three such mills, all on the Isle of Lewis, doing the preliminary work. Each mill carries out the dyeing, blending, carding, spinning and warping of the yarns, the weaving still being done by individual home-based weavers.

While home-based hand-loom weaving continued on Harris, other industries brought the weavers together into mills, but still using hand-looms. H. V. Morton described that tradition when visiting one of Macclesfield's silk mills in 1927, writing:

Macclesfield is the last stronghold of the old hand-loom. The power loom may have conquered the rest of the north, but there are things done in Macclesfield silk which can only be done by hand. There are working in this town about two hundred and fifty hand-loom weavers. They have their own trade union.

In a long shed I heard the slow steady clatter of hand-looms: a sound which Lancashire has now forgotten: the sound to which she rose to greatness.

Contrasted with the uncanny, quick, intelligent, chattering sheds worked by power, this long shed with its sixty deliberate hand-loom weavers, was a surprising glimpse into the past. All the weavers were men. This was so in the old days. The women were spinsters and the men were weavers. One of them allowed me to try the pedal of his loom; he was treading a hundred-weight of lead every time he pedalled…

…The hand-loom is surely the most clumsy instrument in the world. To the untechnical eye it seems more than marvellous that such delicate things as those cobweb threads of coloured silk can be passed through this Heath Robinson-like wilderness of twine, leaden fringe, foot pedals, weighted boulders, shaking arms, and other queer gadgets which beggar description into a tie which 'a man of fashion' buys before he meets 'a lady of quality'.

top: A 1905 postcard showing Tiverton lace-makers leaving John Heathcoat & Co's factory. Built as a water-powered cotton mill, it had been modified for lace manufacture in 1816, and subsequently considerably enlarged and converted to steam. Already a well-established lace-maker, Heathcoat had moved his business to Devon in 1816 after Luddites destroyed his Loughborough factory. The company still operates today.

above: A hand-loom, showing the 'wilderness of twine' which H. V. Morton described.

William Heath Robinson, the eminent cartoonist and illustrator was already at the height of his fame when Morton was writing, his drawings of fantastical and improbable machines widely enjoyed, his name already firmly rooted in everyday language.

top: Raw silk at Macclesfield's Paradise Mill.

above: The complex Jacquard mechanism on a power loom at Macclesfield Silk Museum.

above right: The 2,500hp four-cylinder triple-expansion steam engine which drove 60,000 ring spindles and 24,000 spinning mules in Wigan's Trencherfield Mill. It is the largest mill steam engine in the world still working in its original engine house. Now beautifully restored to working order, it is still regularly steamed.

With restored Jacquard silk looms still operating in Macclesfield's Paradise Mill museum, visitors today can see and hear much of what Morton described nearly ninety years ago.

Demand for fabrics made out of natural materials decreased significantly from the 1970s onwards in the face of competition from a growing range of synthetics – most notably polyesters which could replicate some of the characteristics of wool but at a significantly lower cost – causing the closure of hundreds of mills. Woollen mills in Yorkshire and the Scottish Borders were especially hard hit, putting tens of thousands of spinners, weavers and knitwear makers out of work.

Fine quality wools have experienced a resurgence of interest in recent years, but the days when 'knitwear' automatically meant 'woollen knitwear' are long gone.

Many of the surviving woollen mills now have visitor centres, and some of those offering tours are listed in the gazetteer section.

above: The 1867-built Kittoe & Brotherhood beam engine — perhaps even the prototype — at Coldharbour Woollen Mill, Uffculme, Devon. This engine, typical of the type once used at the mill, originally worked at a Watney Manns brewery in London.

top left: Ian Gammon at work on the spinning frames at Coldharbour, a working woollen mill as well as a museum. In addition to a range of equipment from spinning frames to looms, Coldharbour regularly steams the 19th century steam engines which once powered the mill.

above left: Inside the winding frame of the warping machine, with the completed warp for a length of contract tweed.

above right: Inside Coldharbour's huge 4.3 metre wide waterwheel which drives the mill's line shafts. Rotating today at only 2.5rpm, the wheel, carrying five tons of water, generates about 35hp.

One such mill, Coldharbour Mill in Devon, has seen technology go full circle. Opened as a water-powered woollen mill in the closing years of the 18th century, increasing thirst for power over its working life demanded an eventual change from water to steam. The original 18th century waterwheel was replaced in 1819 with a 4.3 metre wide wheel which could generate 40hp to drive the spinning frames. Gearing increased the wheel's gentle 3.5rpm to the 120rpm of the line shafts which still run throughout the mill today.

Two steam beam engines were installed in the 1860s and 1880s, but they too could not provide the power required by the enlarged mill, being replaced by the 1910 300hp Pollit & Wigzell horizontal engine, still regularly steamed today.

With the present reduced needs of the mill, however, the waterwheel once again provides the drive.

above left: Painted narrowboat, National Waterways Museum, Ellesmere Port,

above right: Preston Corn Mill, East Lothian.

right: Electrically-powered 1951-built colliery winding engine, Big Pit, Blaenafon.

GAZETTEER

WIND & WATER POWER

There are hundreds of working wind and water mills open across the UK, so the following list offers only a sample of the surviving examples of how water and wind powered industry. The website *www.nationalmillsweekend.co.uk* details every mill which is open at least during the national mills weekend event.

Aberdulais Tin Works and Waterfall
www.nationaltrust.org.uk/aberdulais-tinworks-and-waterfall tel: 01639 636674 Aberdulais, Neath, Neath Port Talbot, SA10 8EU Originally a corn mill, an early water-powered tin works was the last industry here. Today the waters of the River Dulais turn the largest electricity-generating waterwheel in Europe.

Alford Windmill
www.alford-windmill.co.uk tel: 01507 462136 32 East Street, Alford, Lincs, LN13 9EH This five-sailed windmill is still in commercial operation. Open daily except Wednesday in July-September, and weekends at other times. Admission charge for mill tour.

Avoncroft Windmill
www.avoncroft.org.uk tel: 01527 831363 Stoke Heath, Bromsgrove, B60 4JR Avoncroft Museum is home to numerous buildings which have been rescued and rebuilt on site. The post mill was built c.1820. Derelict, it was moved to the museum in 1969 and restored to full working order. It has a single pair of millstones, and runs regularly.

Bembridge Windmill
www.nationaltrust.org.uk/bembridge-windmill tel: 01983 873945 High Street, Bembridge, Isle of Wight, PO35 5SQ This Grade I listed building is the last windmill on the Isle of Wight. It still has most of its original machinery. Open March-October. Admission charge.

Bircham Windmill
www.birchamwindmill.co.uk tel: 01485 578393 Snettisham Road, Great Bircham, King's Lynn, PE31 6SJ North Norfolk's oldest working windmill. The machinery and stones were acquired from other derelict mills. Open March-October, admission charge.

Blair Atholl Watermill
www.blairathollwatermill.co.uk tel: 01796 481321 Ford Road, Blair Atholl, PH18 5SH There has been a mill on the site since the 1590s and the restored mill produces a range of oatmeals, wholemeal flour and bread flour. Open daily April to October.

Bursledon Windmill
www3.hants.gov.uk/windmill.htm tel: 0845 603 5635 Windmill Lane, Bursledon, Hampshire, SO31 8BG Grade II listed mill, currently undergoing extensive restoration. Limited access during restoration without charge. Check website for dates and times of opening.

WIND & WATER POWER

Cheddleton Flint Mill
www.cheddletonflintmill.com tel: 0161 408 5083 Leek Road, Cheddleton, Leek, Staffs ST13 7HL Pair of canal-side water-powered flint mills, flint ovens, a period cottage, canal loading dock, a Robey steam engine, and small museum. Free entry.

Claverton Pumping Station
www.claverton.org tel: 01225 483001 Ferry Lane, Claverton, Bath, BA2 7BH Restored 1813 water-powered pumping station designed by John Rennie, built to raise water from the River Avon up to the Kennet and Avon Canal. Check website for operating days.

Cragside Power House
www.nationaltrust.org.uk/cragside tel: 01669 620333 Rothbury, Morpeth, Northumberland, NE65 7PX Early hydro-electric power house, with waterwheel, turbine and generating equipment, which powered the first house in Britain to be lit with Joseph Wilson Swann's electric lights.

Cranbrook Union Windmill
www.unionmill.org.uk 01580-712984 The Hill, Cranbrook, Kent, TN17 3AH England's tallest windmill was built in 1814, and 'modernised' in 1840 to improve its efficiency. Restored 2002-3. Only open some days, free admission. Fabulous website.

Dounby Click Mill
www.historic-scotland.gov.uk/propertyresults/propertydetail.htm?PropID=PL_069 tel: 01856 841815 Dounby, Orkney. The last working horizontal 'Norse' mill in Orkney, Dounby is now restored and in the care of Historic Scotland. Admission free.

Dunham Massey Elizabethan Mill
www.nationaltrust.org.uk/dunham-massey tel: 0161 941 1025 Altrincham, Cheshire, WA14 4SJ This 17th century corn mill on the River Bollin at Dunham Massey was converted to a sawmill in the 1860s. Sawmill machinery still in place. Admission charge.

Eling Tide Mill
www.elingexperience.co.uk tel: 023 8086 9575 Eling Lane, Totton, Hampshire, SO40 9HF There has been a mill on this site on the edge of Southampton Water for over 900 years. The 18th century mill has a pair of waterwheels designed to drive a millstone each.

Forge Mill Needle Museum
www.forgemill.org.uk tel: 01527 464000 Needle Mill Lane, Riverside, Redditch, B98 8HY The only surviving water-powered needle polishing (scouring mill) in the world. Much of the original Victorian water-powered machinery remains and operates on Tuesday afternoons and at weekends.

Heage Windmill
www.heagewindmill.org.uk tel: 01773 853579 Chesterfield Rd, Belper, Derbyshire, DE56 2BH Grade II listed18th century smock mill, rebuilt in the 19th century, again in the early 20th century. Restored to full working order, the mill reopened in 2002.

WIND & WATER POWER

Jordans Mill, Biggleswade
www.jordansmill.com tel: 01767 603940 Langford Road, Broom, Bedfordshire, SG18 9JY
Water-turbine-powered roller mill, converted from stone-milling in late 19th century.
Guided tours only. Check website for times. Admission charge.

Killhope Lead Mines Ore-crushing Mill
www.killhope.org.uk tel: 01388 537505 The North of England Lead Mining Museum,
Cowshill, Upper Weardale, Co. Durham, DL13 1AR The 11m overshot waterwheel
dominates the site. Three other waterwheels on site. Guided tours of the lead mines.

Laxey Wheel
www.laxeywheel.co.uk tel: 01624 648000 Mines Road, Laxey, Isle of Man, IM4 7NL
Designed by the engineer Robert Casement, the wheel was built in 1854 to pump
water from the Glen Mooarpit, part of the Great Laxey complex of lead and zinc
mines. The spectacular 24m high wheel is known as Lady Isabella, after the mine
owner's wife.

Little Salkeld Watermill
www.organicmill.co.uk tel: 01768 881523 Little Salkeld, Penrith, CA10 INN Overshot
watermill, operational and producing stoneground flour by traditional methods. Self-
guided mill tours available, check website for days and times. Small charge.

Maud Foster Windmill
www.maudfoster.co.uk tel: 01205 352188   16 Willoughby Rd, Boston, PE21 9EG
19th century tower mill restored to working order. Limited opening times, so check
website for details. Adjacent building now available as a holiday let.

Museum of East Anglian Life
www.eastanglianlife.org.uk 01449 612229 Stowmarket, Suffolk, IP14 1DL
Eastbridge Windpump drained Minsmere Levels near Leiston, pumping water 2m
from the marshlands into a drainage ditch. Salvaged in 1980s, the pump was rebuilt at
the Museum.

Nether Alderley Mill
www.nationaltrust.org.uk/nether-alderley-mill tel: 01625 527468 Congleton Road,
Nether Alderley, Macclesfield, Cheshire, SK10 4TW 16th century corn mill with two
waterwheels – the water from one turning the other. Converted to steam power in the
1860s. The mill is cared for by the National Trust. Open Tues/Sat/Sun, April-September.

New Abbey Corn Mill
www.historic-scotland.gov.uk/propertyoverview.htm?PropID=PL_220
tel: 01387 850260 New Abbey, Dumfriesshire, DG2 8BX Late 18th century overshot
corn mill now in the care of Historic Scotland.

Outwood Windmill
www.outwoodmill.com tel: 07901 130779 Outwood Common, Outwood, Surrey, RH1
5PW Said to be the oldest working windmill in England, dating back to 1665,
Outwood was designed for one-man operation. At the time of writing, closed due to
storm damage.

WIND & WATER POWER

Preston Mill
www.nts.org.uk/Property/Preston-Mill-and-Phantassie-Doocot tel: 0844 493 2128
Preston Mill, East Linton, Edinburgh, EH40 3DS Undershot corn mill. Guided tours
only. Admission charge.

Quarry Bank Mill
www.nationaltrust.org.uk/quarry-bank tel: 01625 527468 Styal, Wilmslow, Cheshire,
SK9 4LA Five-storey cotton mill, built 1784. Working museum of the cotton industry,
with looms and other machinery, powered by a 50-ton waterwheel and a working
1840s' steam engine. Apprentice House and workers' village nearby.

Saxtead Green Post Mill
www.english-heritage.org.uk/daysout/properties/saxtead-green-post-mill tel: 0870
333 1181 The Mill House, Saxtead Green, Suffolk, IP13 9QQ A post mill rebuilt in the
mid 19th century. Open April-September Friday, Saturday & Bank Holidays.
Admission charge.

Skidby Windmill
www.museums.eastriding.gov.uk/skidby-mill tel: 01482 848405 Skidby, Cottingham,
HU16 5TF A working four-sailed tower mill which still has its original outbuildings,
some of which now house the Museum of East Riding Rural Life.

Stotfold Mill
www.stotfoldmill.com tel: 01462 734541 Mill Lane, Stotfold, Bedfordshire, SG5 4NU
Restored overshot water mill with 4.2m wide iron waterwheel – one of the widest in
the country. Open daily, free admission.

Thwaite Mills Watermill
www.leeds.gov.uk/museumsandgalleries/Pages/Thwaite-Mills-Watermill.aspx
tel: 0113 3782983 Thwaite Lane, Stourton, Leeds, LS10 1RP Water-powered flint mills.
A fulling mill originally stood on the island site, but this was replaced by the present
flint mills in the 19th century. Guided tours Saturday/Sunday.

Tormiston Mill
www.historic-scotland.gov.uk/propertyresults/propertydetail.htm?PropID=PL_292.
tel: 01856 761606 Orkney, KW16 3HA 19th century overshot watermill driving three
pairs of stones, now the visitor centre for the prehistoric site of Maeshowe. Machinery
intact.

Tuxford Windmill
www.tuxford-windmill.co.uk tel: 01777 871202 Retford Rd, Tuxford, Notts, NG22 0NW
The tower mill was built c.1820, and still operates. Guided tours available, but phone
in advance to book.

West Blatchington Windmill
www.sussexmillsgroup.org.uk/blatchington tel: 01273 776017 Holmes Avenue,
Hove, East Sussex, BN3 7LE Unusual six-sided smock mill built circa 1820 on a tall
flint and brick tower. Open Sundays and Bank Holidays only.

WIND & WATER POWER

Willesborough Windmill
www.willesboroughwindmill.co.uk tel: 01233 733416 Mill Lane, Willesborough, Ashford, TN24 0QG A 19th century Grade II listed smock mill, restored in the 1990s, operational most weekends March to October.

Winchester City Mill
www.nationaltrust.org.uk/winchester-city-mill tel: 01962 870057 Bridge Street, Winchester, Hampshire, SO23 0EJ Undershot mill built over the River Itchin, restored and operated by the National Trust. Admission charge.

Woodbridge Tide Mill
www.woodbridgetidemill.org.uk tel: 01394 385295 Tide Mill Way, Woodbridge, Suffolk, IP12 1BY One of only two operational tide mills left in Britain, with a 5m waterwheel. Open daily, April to October, admission charge.

Wortley Top Forge & Industrial Museum
www.topforge.co.uk tel: 0114 2887576 Forge Lane, Thurgoland, South Yorkshire, S35 7DN The oldest surviving Heavy Iron Forge in the world, the water-driven forge, in an early 17th century building, was, from 1840 until 1908, used to forge wrought iron railway axles. It is preserved as it was in 1900. Three waterwheels in working order and the machinery includes hammers cranes. Open Sundays and Bank Holidays.

CANALS

Anderton Boat Lift
www.canalrivertrust.org.uk/Anderton-boat-lift tel: 01606 786777 Lift Lane, Northwich, Cheshire, CW9 6FW The hydraulically-operated Anderton Boat Lift is a two-caisson lift lock providing a 16m vertical link between the River Weaver and the Trent and Mersey Canal. Now fully retored, visitors can take boat trips down the 16m lift, along the River Weaver Navigation and back.

Black Country Living Museum
www.bclm.co.uk tel: 0121 557 9643 Tipton Road, Dudley, DY1 4SQ
By the side of the Dudley Canal, canal-side village, Newcomen engine, vintage trams, and a recreation of a drift mine, all on a 26-acre industrial site.

Crofton Pumping Station
www.croftonbeamengines.org tel: 01672 870300 Crofton, Marlborough, Wiltshire, SN8 3DW Built to pump water to the higher reaches of the Kennet and Avon Canal, the engine house has two beam engines, the older being an 1812 Boulton & Watt engine. The engines are regularly steamed, although the water pumps are now electrically driven.

Claverton Pumping Station
www.claverton.org tel: 01225 483001 Ferry Lane, Claverton, Bath, BA2 7BH
Also built to pump water to the Kennet and Avon, the 1813 pump uses water-power from the River Avon to raise water up 15m into the canal. Check website for operating days.

CANALS

Falkirk Wheel
www.thefalkirkwheel.co.uk tel: 0870 050 0208 Lime Road, Tamfourhill, Falkirk, FK1 4RS
Scotland's Millennium Project restores the link between the Forth & Clyde Canal and
the Union Canal. Boat trips up and down the wheel. Open daily. Free admission, trips
charged.

Foxton Canal Museum
www.fipt.org.uk/museum tel: 0116 279 2657 Middle Lock, Gumley Road, Foxton,
Leicestershire, LE16 7RA Interactive displays,and a wide range of waterway artifacts
tell the story of the Foxton Inclined Plane, the locks, and the Grand Union Canal itself.

Gloucester Waterways Museum
www. canalrivertrust.org.uk/gloucester-waterways-museum tel: 01452 318200
Llanthony Warehouse, The Docks, Gloucester, GL1 2EH Housed in a warehouse in
Gloucester's Victorian Docks, the museum tells the story of navigable canals and
rivers. Boat trips.

Ironbridge Gorge Museum
www.ironbridge.org.uk/our-attractions/museum-of-the-gorge tel: 01952 433424
Coalbrookdale, Shropshire, TF8 7DQ Includes the Hay Inclined Plane, built in the
1790s to raise and lower boats 65m between the Shropshire Union Canal at the top of
the hill and the Coalport Canal at the bottom.

Kennet & Avon Canal Trust
www.katrust.org.uk tel: 01380 721279 Couch Lane, Devizes, SN10 1EB
Small museum with many artifacts. John Rennie's magnificent 16-flight Caen Hill
Locks, now fully operational again, are just a short walk away.

Leawood Pump House
www.middleton-leawood.org.uk tel: 01629 823204 High Peak Wharf, Crompton,
Derbyshire, DE4 5AA Sited by the Cromford Canal, and built in 1849 to raise water
from the River Derwent to the canal. Operates occasionally, check website for
steaming dates.

Linlithgow Canal Centre
www.lucs.org.uk tel: 01506 671215 Manse Rd, Linlithgow, EH49 6AJ Scotland's only
canal museum, the canal centre on the Union Canal also offers boat trips, every
weekend, over the Avon Aqueduct, Scotland's biggest aqueduct.

London Canal Museum
www.canalmuseum.org.uk tel: 020 7713 0836 12-13 New Wharf Rd, London, N1 9RT
This unique waterways museum, by the Regent's Canal, is housed in a former ice
warehouse built in 1862-3 for Carlo Gatti, an ice cream maker, and tells the story of the
ice trade and ice cream as well as the canals. It is London's only waterways museum,
but also an industrial museum.

CANALS

National Waterways Museum
www. canalrivertrust.org.uk/national-waterways-museum tel: 0151 355 5017 South Pier Road, Ellesmere Port, Merseyside, CH65 4FW Located at the northern end of the Shropshire Union Canal where it meets the Manchester Ship Canal at Ellesmere Port, the vast museum includes Telford's dock complex built under the direction of William Jessop, steam pumping station, warehouses filled with boats and other ephemera relating to the history of commerce on the canals, forges, stables and restored workers' cottages. Boat trips available. Admission charge.

Stoke Bruerne Canal Museum
www.canalrivertrust.org.uk/the-canal-museum 01604 862229 Stoke Bruerne, Northants, NN12 7SE Located next to the Grand Union Canal just south of the Blisworth Tunnel, near the village of Stoke Bruerne, the museum tells the story of Britain's canals, the engineers and navvies who built them, and the people who lived and worked on them. Admission charge. Boat trips available.

Yorkshire Waterways Museum
www.waterwaysmuseum.org.uk tel: 01405 768730 Dutch River Side, Goole, DN14 5TB Tells the story of Yorkshire's waterways. Boat trips around Goole Docks. Open daily. Free admission.

MINING

Astley Green Colliery Museum
www.agcm.org.uk tel: 01942 708969 Higher Green Lane, Tyldesley, M29 7JB Includes Lancashire's largest ever steam winding engine. The museum also hosts the largest collection of colliery locomotives in the country, with occasional steaming on 400m of track. Limited opening times – Sundays, Tuesdays, Thursdays – so check website.

Beamish Museum
www.beamish.org.uk tel: 0191 370 4000 Beamish, County Durham, DH9 0RG Huge open air museum includes recreated Victorian town, railway, trams, Beamish Colliery engine house and pit yard. The 1855 colliery winding engine is steamed daily. Drift mine tour. Admission charge.

Black Country Living Museum
www.bclm.co.uk tel: 0121 557 9643 Tipton Road, Dudley, DY1 4SQ Tours of a recreated drift mine, canal-side village, vintage trams, all on a 26-acre industrial site.

Big Pit: National Coal Museum Wales
www.museumwales.ac.uk/en/bigpit tel: 0300 111 2333 Blaenafon, Torfaen, NP4 9XP Part of the Blaenafon World Heritage Site. Preserved mine with underground tours. Extensive site includes a recreation of a coal face with cutting equipment. Superb museum in miners' bathhouse tells the story of the South Wales coalfields. Admission free, charge for car park.

MINING

Cefn Coed Colliery Museum
www.npt.gov.uk tel: 01639 750556 Neath Road, Creunant, SA10 8SN
Tells the story of what was once the world's deepest anthracite mine known as 'The
Slaughterhouse', and the many other anthractie mines in South Wales.

Cleveland Ironstone Mining Museum
www.ironstonemuseum.co.uk tel: 01287 642877 Deepdale, Skinningrove, Saltburn-
by-the-Sea, TS13 4AP Offers an experience of the underground world of the third
largest Cleveland ironstone mine.

Dartmouth Newcomen Engine
www.discoverdartmouth.com tel: 01803 834224 The Engine House, Mayors Avenue,
Dartmouth, TQ6 9YY This, the oldest Newcomen engine in the world, was installed
at Griff Colliery near Coventry in 1725, later moved to Oakthorpe Colliery, Measham,
and eventually to Hawkesbury Junction where it was used as a pump by the Coventry
Canal Company from 1821-1913. It was moved and rebuilt in Dartmouth in 1963 by
the Newcomen Society for demonstration in Newcomen's home town.

Dolaucothi Gold Mine
www.nationaltrust.org.uk/dolaucothi-gold-mines tel: 01558 650177 Pumsaint,
Llanwrda, SA19 8US Includes underground visit to a mine which has been worked
since Roman times. Separate tours of Roman and Victorian workings.

Elsecar Heritage Centre
www.elsecar-heritage-centre.co.uk tel: 01226 740203 Wath Road, Elsecar, South
Yorkshire, S74 8HJ The heritage centre stands on the site of Elsecar New Colliery. The
Newcomen Beam Engine on site ran from 1795 until 1923 when it was replaced by
Electric Pumps. Site includes heritage railway and other ephemera. Admission charge.

Geevor Tin Mine Museum
www.geevor.com tel: 01736 788662 Pendeen, Penzance, Cornwall, TR19 7EW Huge
67-acre site which closed in the 1990s. Includes underground tour led by ex-miners
includes workings from the 18th to 20th centuries. Open daily except Saturdays.

Haig Colliery Mining Museum
www.visitcumbria.com/wc/haig-colliery-mining-museum tel: 01946 599949 Solway
Rd, Kells, Whitehaven, Cumbria, CA28 9BG The remains of Cumbria's last deep mine,
closed in 1986. The winding house is currently under long-term restoration.

Hopewell Colliery Museum
www.fweb.org.uk/local-activity/6-Hopewell_Colliery_Museum tel: 01594 810706
Speech House Rd, Coleford, Gloucestershire, GL16 7EL A working drift mine which
still operates in the winter months, but is open to visitors in summer. Underground
tours.

Ironbridge Gorge Museum
www.ironbridge.org.uk tel: 01952 435900 Coalbrookdale, Shropshire, TF8 7DQ
Huge industrial heritage museum includes the world's first iron bridge, iron foundries,
Coalport China Museum, Victorian town, and a recreated mine at Blists Hill.

MINING

King Edward Mine Museum
www.kingedwardmine.co.uk tel: 01209 614681 Troon, Camborne, Cornwall, TR14 9DP
Much of the machinery in the tin ore processing mill is the last of its kind in the world.
Tours and demonstrations of the machinery. Open daily except Tuesdays and Fridays
in September.

Morwellham Quay
www.morwellham-quay.co.uk tel: 01822 832766 Morwellham, Tavistock, Devon,
PL19 8JL World Heritage Site including port and copper mine. Includes
underground tours of the George and Charlotte copper mine to experience the
conditions of Victorian miners. Open daily, admission charge.

Museum of Cannock Chase
www.wlct.org/cannock/museum tel: 01543 877666 Valley Road, Hednesford, WS12
1TD Includes the Miners Cottage Gallery, Coal Mine Gallery telling the story of coal
mining in the area, and visitors can experience a crawl-through tunnel.

Museum of Lead Mining Wanlockhead
www.leadminingmuseum.co.uk tel: 01659 74387 Wanlockhead, Biggar, Lanarkshire,
ML12 6UT. The museum celebrates an industry which once dominated the area.
Includes underground tour. Nearby is the Wanlockhead Beam Engine. The first beam
engine was erected on the site in 1745, but the present water-bucket engine dates from
the 19th century and operated around the clock.

National Coal Mining Museum for England
www.ncm.org.uk tel: 01924 848806 Caphouse Colliery, Overton, Wakefield, WF4 4RH
Extensive restored pit and museum on the 17 acre site of Hope Pit. Includes 1876
steam winding engine. Underground tours 130m below ground. Experience the lives
of coal miners in the museum's new 'Go Mining' interactive tour. Extensive
exhibitions of memorabilia and photographs in the former miners' baths. Free
admission.

National Mining Museum Scotland
www.scottishminingmuseum.com tel: 0131 663 7519 Newtongrange, Dalkeith,
Mid-lothian, EH22 4QN The Lady Victoria Colliery, mothballed in 1981 is Europe's
most complete surviving Victorian and Edwardian mine. Recreation of underground
roadway and coal face.

North of England Lead Mining Museum
www.killhope.org.uk tel: 01388 537505 near Cowshill, Upper Weardale, County
Durham, DL13 1AR A fully restored 19th century lead mine. Collection of early
mining machinery, large waterwheel on site. The 11m overshot waterwheel which
powered the ore crusher dominates the site. Underground tour of Park Level Mine.

Peak District Lead Mining Museum
www.peakdistrictleadminingmuseum.co.uk tel: 01629 583834 South Parade, Matlock,
Derbyshire DE4 3NR Recreation of a lead mine in the former Matlock Bath Pavilion.
Across the road is Temple Mine, with underground tours at noon and 1400 hours.

MINING

Poldark Mine
www.poldarkmine.org.uk tel: 01326 573173 Wendron, Helston, Cornwall, TR13 7SX
Originally known as Wheal Roots, the 18th century tin mine includes the only Cornish
beam engine still pumping water from a mine, albeit now powered by electricity.

Prestongrange Museum
www.prestongrange.org tel: 0131 6532904 Morison's Haven, Prestonpans, East
Lothian, EH32 9RX An important centre of Scotland's Industrial Revolution,
Prestongrange had a 16th century harbour, 17th century glass works, 18th and 19th
century potteries, and a 19th-20th century coal mine and brick works. The Cornish
Beam Engine and Engine House are unique as the only beam engine in Scotland still
on its original site.

South Wales Miners Museum
www.swmm.co.uk tel: 01639 851 833 Afan Forest Park, Cynonville, Neath, Port
Talbot, SA13 3HG Displays include photographs, documents, early mining
equipment, and a recreated miner's cottage. Admission charge.

Summerlee Museum of Scottish Industrial Life
www.northlanarkshire.gov.uk/summerlee tel: 01236 638460 Heritage Way,
Coatbridge, ML5 1QD The museum collection, on the site for the former Summerlee
Ironworks, includes an 1810 winding engine, the only surviving example of a
Newcomen rotative engine. It came from Farme Colliery in Rutherglen. The museum
also displays the 1924 winding engine from the former Cardowen Colliery at Shotts.

Sygun Copper Mine
www.syguncoppermine.co.uk tel: 01766 890595 Beddgelert, Gwynedd, LL55 4NE
Self-guided underground audio tour takes visitors through winding tunnels and
underground caverns into the heart of a Victorian copper mine. Open daily March to
end of October. Admission charge.

Washington 'F' Pit
www.twmuseums.org.uk/washington tel: 0191 553 2323 Albany Way, Washington,
NE37 1BJ The winding house and headgear of the former F Pit, which ceased
production in 1968 are preserved, having been gifted to the people of Washington by
the NCB. The winding engine is now electrically driven. Free seasonal admission.

Woodhorn Museum and Northumberland Archives
www.experiencewoodhorn.com tel: 01670 624455 Queen Elizabeth II Country Park,
Ashington, Northumberland, NE63 9YF The listed Ashington Colliery buildings are
said to be the finest surviving late 19th and early 20th century examples in the North
East of England.

Yorkshire Dales Mining Museum
www.yorkshiredalesminingmuseum.com tel: 01282 841422 School Lane, Earby,
Barnoldswick, Lancs, BB18 6QF Fascination collection of ephemera, housed in the
Old Grammar School. Open summer Sundays.

IRON & STEEL

Abbeydale Industrial Hamlet
www.simt.co.uk/abbeydale-industrial-hamlet tel: 0114 272 2106 Abbeydale Road South, Sheffield, S7 2QW   A water-powered toolworks used in the manufacture of knives, scythes and other tools. The 1830 Crucible Furnace at Abbeydale is the only one of its kind in the world which still survives intact. The 1785 Tilt Forge houses two huge tilt hammers, and the 1817 Grinding Hull had 6 water-powered grindstones and 2 glazing stones. Open daily except Friday & Saturday. Admission charge.

Black Country Living Museum
www.bclm.co.uk tel: 0121 557 9643 Tipton Road, Dudley, West Midlands, DY1 4SQ This broad-based industrial museum contains a typical Black Country hand rolling mill in which iron and later, steel bars were reduced in size or changed in section. Also on site are forges and other items relating to the local iron and steel industries. When in operation today, the mill is now driven by an electric motor.

Blaenafon Ironworks
www.cadw.wales.gov.uk/daysout/blaenavonironworks tel: 01495 792615 North Street, Blaenavon, NP4 9RN Extensive remains of late 18th century ironworks, expanded and developed in the 19th century. In 2000 Blaenavon was awarded World Heritage Site status for the industrial landscape including the Ironworks and the nearby Big Pit. The ironworks site includes furnaces, the impressive Balance Tower, workers cottages and a recreation of the workers' shop. Open daily, admission free.

Bonawe Ironworks
www.historic-scotland.gov.uk/propertyresults tel: 01866 822432 Taynuilt, PA35 1JQ The most complete charcoal-burning ironworks in Britain, Bonawe was established in 1753 by Loch Etive. The furnace survives largely intact, together with two vast charcoal stores and other buildings. An exhibition charts the history of the iron furnace, and the chemistry of iron making. Cannonballs and iron pigs cast at the furnace are displayed.

Finch Foundry
www.nationaltrust.org.uk/finch-foundry tel: 01837 840046 Sticklepath, Okehampton, Devon, EX20 2NW The last working water-powered forge in England, still with much of its machinery including trip hammers, grindstones and the foundry itself which, at its peak, produced about 400 edge tools every day. Regular demonstrations.

Ironbridge Gorge Museum
www.ironbridge.org.uk/our-attractions/coalbrookdale-museum-of-iron tel: 01952 433424 Coalbrookdale, Shropshire, TF8 7DQ   The Coalbrookdale Museum of Iron is one of the ten Ironbridge Gorge Museums which include the world's first iron bridge, iron foundries, Coalport China Museum, Victorian town, and a recreated mine at Blists Hill.

IRON & STEEL

Kelham Island Museum
www.simt.co.uk/kelham-island-museum Tel: 0114 272 2106 Alma Street, Sheffield, S3 8RY Explores the history of steelmaking, its origins, the inventions, the workers, the products, from Benjamin Huntsman's invention of crucible steel in 1742, to Bessemer's mass production method in 1856, and Harry Brearley's discovery of stainless steel in 1913. On display is one of the last 25 ton converters in the world, used by British Steel at Workington until 1974.

Magna Science Adventure Centre
www.visitmagna.co.uk Tel: 01709 720002 Sheffield Road, Templeborough. Rotherham, S60 1DX Set in the former Steel, Peech and Tozer steelworks, Magna sets out to tell the story of steel-making. One of the steelworks' original electric arc furnaces is brought back to life everyday with pyrotechnics, audio and smoke to re-create the atmosphere of the steel-making process. The steelworks closed in 1993 but its industrial past is obvious, with hulking hooks, winding passages, cupolas and cranes still in position.

National Slate Museum
www.museumwales.ac.uk/slate Tel: 0300 111 2333 Llanberis, Gwynedd, LL55 4TY The foundry manufactured iron and brass tools and equipment for the Welsh slate industry. The brass furnace is operated periodically. Check website for details.

Shepherd Wheel, Sheffield
www.simt.co.uk/shepherd-wheel-workshop Tel: 0114 2722106 Whiteley Woods, off Hangingwater Road, Sheffield, S11 2YE The museum includes a water wheel, two grinding hulls and water-powered grinding wheels, buffers and other equipment used in the finishing of steel cutlery and knives. There is a collection of tools and equipment on display in the grinding hulls. Reopened in 2012 after a Heritage Lottery funded upgrade, the museum offers regular demonstrations of the grinder's craft.

Summerlee Museum of Scottish Industrial Life
www.northlanarkshire.gov.uk/summerlee Tel: 01236 638460 Heritage Way, Coatbridge, ML5 1QD The museum collection, on the site for the former Summerlee Ironworks, includes a rich assortment of material relating to Scotland iron and steel industry. The foundations of the Summerlee Ironworks can be seen from a viewing platform.

Tata Steel Scunthorpe
www.afrps.co.uk Tel: 01652 657053 Entrance E, Brigg Road, Scunthorpe, North Lincolnshire, DN16 1BP The Appleby Frodingham Railway Preservation Society operates regular railtours around Tata Steel's working Scunthorpe works – a unique opportunity to see the exterior facilities at a working steel works by train. No photography permitted except in loco sheds. Check website for dates and times. Advance booking is essential.

above left: The rebuilt paddle steamer PS *Medway Queen* being towed out of the drydock in Bristol after construction of her new hull was completed in 2013.

above right: Leaving Cranmore Station — a passenger's view on the East Somerset Railway.

left: The engine-man operating the main steam valve on the single-cylinder winding engine at Blists Hill, Ironbridge Gorge World Heritage Site. The engine, which dates from c.1870, was relocated to the Blists Hill Mine site in 1970 from Milburgh Tileries near Jackfield in Shropshire.

RAILWAYS

Beamish Musem
www.beamish.org.uk   tel: 0191 370 4000 Beamish, County Durham, DH9 0RG
Ride behind replicas of Steam Elephant or Puffing Billy on the Pockerley Waggonway.
Steam at the rebuilt Rowley Station every weekend and occasional live steam on the
Colliery Railway system (special events and the first weekend of each month).

Bluebell Railway
www.bluebell-railway.co.uk   tel: 01825 720800   Sheffield Park Station, East Sussex,
TN22 3QL   The 9 mile line from Sheffield Park to Kingscote runs on London Brighton
& South Coast Railway trackbed. The Bluebell has the largest collection of preserved
Southern Railway locomotives.

Bodmin & Wenford Railway
www.bodminrailway.co.uk   tel: 01208 73555 General Station, Bodmin, Cornwall,
PL31 1AQ   From Bodmin Central, the railway operates a 6.5 mile line running north-
west to Boscarne Junction and south-east to Bodmin Parkway. Trains operate
weekends February to December, daily late May to early October.

Buckinghamshire Railway Centre
www.bucksrailcentre.org   tel: 01296 655720 Quainton Road Station, nr Aylesbury,
Buckinghamshire, HP22 4BY A working steam museum on a 25 acre site. Exhibits
range from express passenger locomotives to the humble shunting engine. Many of
the mainline locomotives are under restoration.

Bo'ness & Kinneil Railway
www.srps.org.uk/railway   tel: 01506 822298 Bo'ness Station, Union Street, Bo'ness,
West Lothian, EH51 9AQ   Operated by the Scottish Railway Preservation Society.
Trains run between Bo'ness and Manuel. Trains steam hauled by historic locomotives.
Historic station buildings from various locations all over Scotland. Open days and
special events.

Caledonian Railway
www.caledonianrailway.com   tel: 01356 622992 The Station, Park Road, Brechin,
Angus, DD9 7AF   Reviving an historic name on a 4 mile length of track from the
Victorian station at Brechin to Bridge of Dun. Steam trains run on Sundays from
Easter to September, diesels at other times.

Chinnor & Princes Risborough Railway
www.chinnorrailway.co.uk   tel: 01844 353535 Station Approach, Station Road,
Chinnor, Oxfordshire, OX39 4ER A working railway with the majority of the trains
being diesel-hauled. There are numerous steam days throughout the season, usually
with one locomotive in steam.

Churnet Valley Railway
www.churnet-valley-railway.co.uk   tel: 01538 750755 Kingsley & Froghall Station,
Froghall, Staffordshire, ST10 2HA Operated by Churnet Valley Railway (1992) plc.
Steam services operate on a 10.5 mile line from Froghall to Cheddleton most
weekends and Bank Holidays with BR, USA and guest locomotives.

RAILWAYS

Dartmouth Steam Railway
www.dartmouthrailriver.co.uk   tel: 01803 555872   Queens Park Station, Torbay Rd, Paignton, Devon, TQ4 6AF   Operated by the Dartmouth Steam Railway & River Boat Company. The 7 mile route from Paignton to Kingswear runs steam services from April to October plus the usual Santa Specials.

Didcot Railway Centre
www.didcotrailwaycentre.org.uk   tel: 01235 817200   Didcot, Oxfordshire, OX11 7NJ   Huge collection of GWR locomotives, rolling stock and ephemera. The Didcot collection is said to be the largest collection representing a single company anywhere in the world. Standard gauge and broad gauge.

East Lancashire Railway
www.eastlancsrailway.org.uk   tel: 0161 764 7790   Bury Bolton Street Station, Bolton Street, Bury, Lancashire, BL9 0EY Operates over a 12 mile track between Heywood and Rawtenstall every weekend and additional days from May to September. Large collection of locomotives. Open days and steam galas attract visiting locomotives.

East Somerset Railway
www.eastsomersetrailway.com   tel: 01749 880417   Cranmore Station, West Cranmore, Shepton Mallet, Somerset, BA4 4QP A 5 mile round trip through the Mendip countryside on the line set up by the artist David Shepherd, starts in the historic station buildings brought to Cranmore from Wells and Westbury-sub-Mendip.

Ecclesbourne Valley Railway
www.e-v-r.com   tel: 01629 823076   Wirksworth Station, Station Road, Coldwell Street, Wirksworth, DE4 4FB   Operated by WyvernRail plc. While the majority of services are diesel, steam-hauled services are run on the 8.5-mile line between Duffield and Ravenstor, the last half mile of which is up a 1 in 27 incline.

Embsay & Bolton Abbey Railway
www.embsayboltonabbeyrailway.org.uk   tel: 01756 710614   Bolton Abbey Station, Bolton Abbey, Skipton, North Yorks, BD23 6AF Operated by Yorkshire Dales Railway Museum Trust (Holdings) Limited. Industrial steam locomotives haul team trains between Embsay Station and Bolton Abbey every Sunday and most days in the summer.

Foxfield Light Railway
www.foxfieldrailway.co.uk   tel: 01782 396210   Caverswall Road Station, Blythe Bridge, Stoke on Trent, ST11 9BG   A 5.5 mile round trip from Caverswell Road Station to Dilhorne Park on a line originally built to serve Foxfield Colliery. Industrial steam locomotives include Haydock Foundry's 1874-built *Bellerophon*.

Gloucestershire Warwickshire Railway
www.gwsr.com   tel: 01242 621405   The Railway Station, Toddington, Gloucs, GL54 5DT Revelling in the initials 'GWR', the railway operates on 10 miles of track between Toddington and Cheltenham Racecourse, using a mixture of GWR and BR locomotives, including 9F *Black Prince*.

RAILWAYS

Great Central Railway

www.gcrailway.co.uk tel: 01509 632323 Great Central Station, Great Central Road, Loughborough, LE11 1RW. The Great Central operates an 8 mile section of the former London to Sheffield main line between Loughborough and Leicester, and is the only double-track heritage line in the UK.

Gwili Railway

www.gwili-railway.co.uk tel: 01267 238213 Bronwydd Arms Station, Carmarthen, SA33 6HT The railway operates a short track from Bronwydd to Danycoed and on to Llwyfan Cerrig, and is the only standard gauge railway operating steam services in South West Wales. 2010 was the line's 150th anniversary.

Keighley & Worth Valley Railway

www.kwvr.co.uk tel: 01535 645214 The Railway Station, Haworth, Keighley, West Yorkshire, BD22 8NJ Running from Oxenhope to Keighley, this line was rescued immediately after BR closure. With over 30 locomotives, several of them steamed regularly, the K&WR remains one of Britain's most popular railways.

Kent & East Sussex Railway

www.kesr.org.uk tel: 01580 765155 Tenterden Town Station, Station Rd, Tenterden, Kent, TN30 6HE Running 10.5 miles from Tenterden Town to Bodiam, the Kent & East Sussex Railway's steam-hauled services feature tank engines with Southern Railway or military backgrounds.

Lakeside & Haverthwaite Railway

www.lakesiderailway.co.uk tel: 01539 531594 Haverthwaite Station, nr Ulverston, Cumbria, LA12 8AL Operated by Lakeside & Haverthwaite Railway Co. Ltd. Steam trains run 3.5 miles between Haverthwaite and Lakeside on Windermere. L&HR operates the only preserved Fairburn 2-6-4 tanks.

Lavender Line

www.lavender-line.co.uk tel: 01825 750515 Isfield Station, Isfield, Nr Uckfield, East Sussex, TN22 5XB Steam trains operate most Sundays on a short track between Isfield and Little Horsted. Most trains are hauled by one or other of a pair of small saddle tanks.

Locomotion

www.nrm.org.uk tel: 01388 771448 Shildon, Co Durham, DL4 1PQ
The National Railway Museum at Shildon is home to a large part of the National Railway Collection, displayed in a superb new exhibition hall. Primarily a museum of classic locomotives, rolling stock and ephemera.

Mid-Hants Railway

www.watercressline.co.uk tel: 01962 733810 Station Road, Alresford, Hampshire, SO24 9JG The Watercress Line runs for 10 miles from New Alresford to Alton. Steam services run most weekends, and daily in summer. Large roster of locomotives from Southern Railways, LMS and BR Southern Region.

RAILWAYS

Middleton Railway
www.middletonrailway.org.uk tel: 0845 680 1758   The Station, Moor Road, Hunslet, Leeds, LS10 2JQ Operated by The Middleton Railway Trust Ltd. Industrial steam and diesel locomotives head trains Saturdays, Sundays, Bank Holiday Mondays and Wednesdays in August.

Midland Railway Centre
www.midlandrailway-butterley.co.uk tel: 01773 747674 Butterley Station, Ripley, Derbyshire, DE5 3QZ Both steam and diesel run on the 3.5 mile track from Buttelry to Hammersmith. Locomotive sheds and museum at Swanwick, home of the Princess Royal Class Locomotive Trust

National Railway Museum
www.nrm.org.uk tel: 08448 153139 Leeman Road, York, YO26 4XJ 200 years of railway history. The collections include over 100 locomotives, some 250 items of rolling stock and the most extensive collection of early railway ephemera anywhere in the world. The museum is also home to a vast archive of photographs and documents relating to the history of Britain's railways.

Nene Valley Railway
www.nvr.org.uk tel: 01780 784444 Wansford Station, Stibbington, Peterborough, PE8 6LR Describing itself as 'the international railway', the NVR has an extensive collection of British, Polish, Swedish and German locomotives, and operates a 5.5 mile line from Peterborough to Yarwell Junction.

North Norfolk Railway
www.nnrailway.co.uk tel: 01263 820800 Sheringham Station, Station Approach, Sheringham, Norfolk, NR26 8RA A 10.5 mile round trip through the Norfolk countryside from Sheringham to Holt, steam-hauled in summer. Steam galas are often boosted by visits from guest locomotives.

North Yorkshire Moors Railway
www.nymr.co.uk tel: 01751 472508 12 Park Street, Pickering, North Yorkshire, YO18 7AJ Running through the North Yorkshire Moors National Park, the railway operates an 18-mile line between Pickering and Grosmont, and on specific days, the 24 mile Esk Valley line between Whitby and Battersby via Grosmont where there are engine sheds and a visitor centre.

Peak Rail
www.peakrail.co.uk tel: 01629 580381 Matlock Station, Matlock, Derbyshire , DE4 3NA An ex-WD J94 regularly hauls trains on 4 miles of track between Rowsley South and Matlock Riverside, on what was once part of the Midland Railway's route from Manchester Central to London St Pancras.

Ribble Steam Railway
www.ribblesteam.org.uk tel: 01772 253731 Chain Caul Road, Preston, Lancashire, PR2 2PD The railway has a collection of more than 40 historic industrial locomotives, and steam-hauled services operate on the 1.5 mile track, weekends, April to September. Mainline locomotives on display.

KITTOE & BROTHE
ENGINEERS & MILLWR
LONDON.
1867.

above left: *Moorbarrow* taking on water, East Somerset Railway.

above right: Detail of the engine control linkages on *Holland 1*, Britain's first submarine, now displayed at the Submarine Museum, Gosport.

left: The engine gearing on the restored Balloch Steam Winch, used to haul steamers out of Loch Lomond. The winch is regularly steamed during the summer months.

opposite page: The governor on the magnificent Kittoe & Brotherhood beam engine now displayed, and regularly steamed, at Coldharbour Mill in Devon.

RAILWAYS

Royal Deeside Railway
www.deeside-railway.co.uk   tel: 01330 844416 Milton of Crathes, Banchory, Kincardineshire, AB32 5QH Operated by The Deeside Railway Company Limited. Limited number of steam days, using Barclay 0-4-0ST *Bon Accord.*

Severn Valley Railway
www.svr.co.uk   tel: 01299 403816   The Railway Station, Bewdley, Worcestershire, DY12 1BG   Operates over a 16 mile track carrying more than 250,000 passengers between Bridgenorth and Kidderminster Town, through scenery which captures the essence of a Victorian branch-line.

South Devon Railway
www.southdevonrailway.co.uk   tel: 01364 644370   The Station, Dartbridge Road, Buckfastleigh, South Devon, TQ11 0DZ Running 7 miles from Totnes Littlehempston to Buckfastleigh, the SDR celebrated its 45th anniversary in 2014. Operates services daily from late March until the end of October and on other occasional dates.

Spa Valley Railway
www.spavalleyrailway.co.uk   tel: 01892 537715 West Station, Nevill Ter, Royal Tunbridge Wells, Kent, TN2 5QY   Railway runs for 5.25 miles between Eridge and Tunbridge Wells via Groombridge and High Rocks. Steam services hauled by a number of locomotives.

Strathspey Railway
www.strathspeyrailway.co.uk   tel: 01479 810725   Aviemore Station, Dalfaber Road, Aviemore, Inverness-shire, PH22 1PY Operated by the Strathspey Railway Company Ltd.   Trains operate on 10 miles of track from Aviemore to Broomhill. With catering on the trains, you can enjoy afternoon tea while being hauled by historic steam locomotives.

Swanage Railway
www.swanagerailway.co.uk tel: 01929 425800   Railway Station Approach, Swanage, Dorset, BH19 1HB Running 6 miles from Swanage, past Corfe Castle, to Norden, steam services hauled by mainline locomotives operate daily from late March to the end of October, pluse special weekends and galas.

Swindon & Cricklade Railway
www.swindon-cricklade-railway.org   tel: 01793 771615 Blunsdon Station, Tadpole Lane, Blunsdon, Swindon, SN25 2DA   Currently running from Taw Valley Halt to South Meadow Lane, there are long-term plans to extend the line north to Cricklade and south to Mouldon Hill Park. The line uses part of the trackbed of the former Midland & South Western Junction Railway.

Tanfield Railway
www.tanfield-railway.co.uk   tel: 01506 822298   Marley Hill Engine Shed, Old Marley Hill, Gateshead, NE16 5ET Claiming to be the world's oldest railway, with a trackbed dating in part from 1725! The railway has an extensive collection of historic industrial locomotives, and steam services operate on most Sundays.

Weardale Railway
www.weardale-railway.org.uk   tel: 01388 526203   Stanhope Station, Stanhope, Bishop Auckland, Co. Durham, DL13 2YS Operated by The Weardale Railway Trust Ltd. The company is reviving one of the oldest branch lines in the country as a heritage railway. The trust runs weekend steam services from Stanhope to Bishop Auckland West.

West Somerset Railway
www.west-somerset-railway.co.uk   tel: 01643 704996   The Railway Station, Minehead, Somerset, TA24 5BG.   20 Miles, 10 stations, and a true GWR branch line experience. Trains runs from Bishops Lydeard to Minehead, much of it along spectacular coastline. The S&DR Trust is based at Washford Station.

SHIPPING & SHIPBUILDING

Arctic Corsair
www.hullcc.gov.uk/museums   tel: 01482 300300   Streetlife Museum of Transport, High Street, Hull, HU1 1PS The last Hull 'sidewinder' side-trawler built at Beverley 1960. Fished off Iceland, Greenland, Newfoundland until 1987. Now fully restored to 1960s' condition. Visitors are can visit the main deck, bridge, radio & engine rooms, messroom, galley, fishrooms.

MV *Balmoral*
www.waverleyexcursions.co.uk tel: 0845 130 4647 36 Lancefield Quay, Glasgow, G3 8HA   The 688grt *Balmoral* is, at the time of writing, back in Bristol after undergoing survey and refit work at Sharpness, and should be back in service in 2015. Built by Thornycroft in Woolston in 1949 as an Isle of Wight ferry, she has been an excursion vessel since 1986.

Barrow Dock Museum
www.dockmuseum.org.uk tel: 01229 876400 North Road, Barrow-in-Furness, Cumbria, LA14 2PW Built in an historic graving dock, the museum is home to a wealth of objects and information on Barrow's shipbuilding heritage. Contains the photographic archive of the Vickers shipyard, ship models and other ephemera.

HMS *Belfast*
www.iwm.org.uk/visits/hms-belfast tel: 0207 940 6300 The Queen's Walk, London, SE1 2JH Built by Harland & Wolff of Belfast, the 11,553 ton 'Edinburgh Class' cruiser entered service in 1939. Moored in the Thames since 1971, she is open daily.

HMY *Britannia*
www.royalyachtbritannia.co.uk   tel: 0131 555 5566 Ocean Terminal, Leith, Edinburgh, EH6 6JJ The elegant lines of this iconic vessel have been compromised in the cause of visitor comfort, but in her new berth it is now possible to explore the 5,800 ton John Brown Clyde-built steam turbine yacht.

Chatham Historic Dockyard
www.thedockyard.co.uk tel: 01634 823800 The Historic Dockyard, Chatham, Kent, ME4 4TZ Collection includes: HMS *Cavalier* was the Royal Navy's last operational World War II destroyer; the 1878 steam and sail iron-framed sloop HMS *Gannet*, built at Sheerness, and renamed the TS *Mercury* in 1913. Also displayed is the 1962-built HM submarine *Ocelot*.

SHIPPING & SHIPBUILDING

Clipper Ship *Cutty Sark*

www.rmg.co.uk/cuttysark tel: 020 8312 6608 King William Walk, Greenwich, London, SE10 9HT The rebuilt clipper, built on the Clyde at Dumbarton in 1869, is now in her new elevated position over the drydock, the ship's new setting allowing visitors to walk beneath her keel.

RRS *Discovery*

www.rrsdiscovery.com tel: 01382 309060 Discovery Quay, Riverside Drive, Dundee, Angus, DD1 4XA Scott's 1901 Dundee-built ship on which he sailed to the Antarctic is part restoration, part reconstruction, and fitted out to look as she did on her most famous voyage.

TSS *Duke of Lancaster*

Not open to the public Llanerch-y-Mor, Mostyn, Flintshire. Embedded in a sand-filled drydock, the former Irish Sea ferry is a reminder of the perils associated with trying to preserve a large steamship and use it for a new purpose. Exterior only is viewable.

Glasgow Riverside Museum

www.glasgowlife.org.uk tel: 0141 287 2720 100 Pointhouse Road, Glasgow, G3 8RS Built on the site of the former Pointhouse Shipyard, Glasgow's new museum contains a wealth of information on Clyde shipbuilding. Moored at the quay is the barque *Glenlee* built at the Bay Yard in Port Glasgow in 1896 and now restored.

Gosport Royal Navy Submarine Museum

www.submarine-museum.co.uk tel: 023 9251 0354 Haslar Rd, Gosport, Hampshire, PO12 2AS The Museum has three British submarines in its collection – HMS *Alliance*, built by Vickers in Barrow in 1945, Britain's first submarine, the 1901-built *Holland I* and the World War II midget submarine *X24*. The forty-minute tour inside HMS *Alliance* is unmissable.

SS *Great Britain*

www.ssgreatbritain.org tel: 0117 926 0680 Great Western Dockyard, Gas Ferry Road, Bristol, BS1 6TY Brunel's great 1844 ship, the world's first propellor-driven passenger ship, was rebuilt from the hulk which returned to Bristol in 1979. The project was completed in 2005 and she is open to visitors daily.

Hartlepool's Maritime Experience

www.hartlepoolsmaritimeexperience.com tel: 01429 860077 Maritime Ave, Hartlepool, Cleveland, TS24 0XZ Three museums on the same site – Hartlepool Maritime Museum, the 1817 Mumbai-built HMS *Trincomalee* and former Humber ferry PS *Wingfield Castle* built In Hartlepool in 1934 by William Gray & Co, as was her sister PS *Tattershall Castle*.

PS *Kingswear Castle*

www.kingswearcastle.co.uk tel: 01803 555872 5 Lower Street, Dartmouth, TQ6 9AJ Built in Dartmouth in 1924, originally for use on the River Dart, the restored paddle steamer returned to the Dart and started operating on her home river again at Easter 2013. After years working out of Chatham, she now offers cruises from Dartmouth up-river as far as Totnes.

SHIPPING & SHIPBUILDING

Lydia Eva & Mincarlo Trust

www.lydiaeva.org.uk tel: 07927 602934   15 Milton Road East, Lowestoft, Suffolk, NR32 1NT The Trust preserved two important fishing vessels, both of which are open to the public – the Yarmouth Steam Drifter *Lydia Eva* YH89 is based at Great Yarmouth, and the Lowestoft Side Winder Trawler *Mincarlo* LT412 at Lowestoft Quay. Free admission, donations welcome.

PS *Maid of the Loch*

www.maidoftheloch.org tel: 01389 711865 Loch Lomond Steamship Co, The Pier, Pier Road, Balloch, G83 8QX The largest paddle steamer ever to sail on Britain's inland waters, and the last ever built on the Clyde, the 1953-built *Maid of the Loch* is undergoing a restoration programme designed to bring her back into steam. The restored Balloch Steam Winch used to haul the steamer out of the loch, built in 1902, is also open and regularly in steam. Free admission.

PS *Medway Queen*

www.medwayqueen.co.uk   tel: 01634 575717 Gillingham Pier, Western Arm, Pier Approach Road, Gillingham, Kent, ME7 1RX Built at Troon in 1924 for the New Medway Steam Packet Company, for work on the River Medway. Abandoned and sunk in the 1970s, raised in 1987 and currently being rebuilt.

Merseyside Maritime Museum

www.liverpoolmuseums.org.uk/maritime tel: 0151 478 4499 Albert Dock, Liverpool L3 4AQ The museum reflects the history and importance of the Port of Liverpool. Extensive collection of over 2000 ship models, mostly merchant vessels – from steamships to sailing ships, builders models to ships in bottles. The museum also offers tours of the Mersey pilot boat MV *Edmund Gardner*.

National Maritime Museum

www.rmg.co.uk/national-maritime-museum tel. 020 8858 4422 Romney Road, Greenwich, London, SE10 9NF The National Maritime Museum is the museum for anything to do with shipping and maritime history. On display and worked now by electricity, is the starboard engine from the steam tug *Old Trafford/Reliant*.

SS *Nomadic*

www.nomadicbelfast.com Hamilton Dry Dock, off Queen's Road, Queen's Island, Belfast, BT3 9DT *Nomadic* was built by Harland and Wolff in 1911 as a tender for the White Star Line liners *Titanic, Olympic* and *Britannic*. The last of her type, she is undergoing restoration. Exterior only viewable.

Portsmouth Historic Dockyard

www.historicdockyard.co.uk tel: 023 9298 4316 Victory Gate, H M Naval Base, Main Road, Portsmouth, PO1 3LJ Vessels include HMS *Victory*, Nelson's flagship currently undergoing a major restoration, HMS *Warrior*, Britain's only preserved battleship – this iron-hulled design from 1860 has been almost completely rebuilt, to offer visitors a chance to experience what life on a warship was like 150 years ago – Henry VIII's flagship *Mary Rose*, now dryng out in her new museum, and Gallipoli veteran HMS *Monitor M33 (Minerva)*, built in 1915. The WWII submarine HMS *Alliance* is preserved at Gosport.

above left: A model
ship hull under test
in the Denny Ship
Model Experiment
Tank at the Scottish
Maritime Museum,
Dumbarton.

above right: The
newly restored
Gallipoli veteran
warship HMS *Monitor
M33* (Minerva) in her
drydock at
Portsmouth's Historic
Dockyard.

right: The diesel
engines fitted in 1920
to the tall ship
Glenlee when she
was re-registered as
the *Clarastella*. The
restored vessel is
moored at Pointhouse
Quay, Glasgow.

SHIPPING & SHIPBUILDING

Scottish Maritime Museum Dumbarton

www.scottishmaritimemuseum.org tel. 01389 763444 Castle Street, Dumbarton, Dunbartonshire, G82 1QS The 100m long Denny Ship Model Experiment Tank where ship hull designs were tested is a unique survival from the great days of Clyde shipbuilding. The 1823 side-lever engine designed by Robert Napier for the PS *Leven* is on display outside.

Scottish Maritime Museum Irvine

www.scottishmaritimemuseum.org tel. 01294 278283 Harbour Road, Irvine, Ayrshire, KA12 8QE The Irvine site includes many detailed ship models, marine steam engines, and other artifacts, displayed in the rebuilt Linthouse Engine Shop dating from 1872, where the steam engines for many fine vessels were constructed. The building, from the Linthouse yard of Alexander Stephen & Sons in Govan, was re-erected on the Irvine site in the 1980s. PS *Waverley's* original 1946 boiler stands outside.

SS *Shieldhall*

www.ss-shieldhall.co.uk tel: 0844 3572329 Berth 29, Southampton Docks, SO14 3XD Built by Lobnitz & Co. at Renfrew on the Clyde in 1955, Shieldhall is the largest surviving passenger/cargo steamship in Britain, and she is still sailing regularly. She is still powered by her original triple-expansion engines. Available for cruises and private hire, and bookings can be arranged through the website.

SS *Sir Walter Scott*

www.lochkatrine.com/about/steamship-sir-walter-scott tel: 01877 376315 Trossachs Pier, Loch Katrine, by Callander, Stirling, FK17 8HZ Much modified since her launch in 1900, the steamer still regularly sails the loch. Now fired by bio-fuel, but still with her original 3-cylinder triple expansion steam engine powered by two locomotive-type boilers.

PS *Waverley*

www.waverleyexcursions.co.uk tel: 0845 130 4647 Waverley Terminal, 36 Lancefield Quay, Glasgow, G3 8HA Britain's last sea-going paddle-steamer, *Waverley* is a regular summer sight around Britain's coast. Built on the Clyde by A & J Inglis in 1947, a 2000-2003 refit largely restored her to her 1940s' appearance.

TRADE & MANUFACTURE

Beamish Museum
www.beamish.org.uk tel: 0191 370 4000 Beamish, County Durham, DH9 0RG
Huge open air museum includes recreated Victorian town, railway, trams, Beamish
Colliery engine house and pit yard. Hand-made confectionery demonstrations in the
sweetie shop. In Joseph Herron's Bakery watch bakers at work using traditional
methods to make bread, cakes and pies. Typical small-town garage, including a 1907
Armstrong-Whitworth car and motorcycles on display in the showroom. The 1855
colliery winding engine is steamed daily. Admission charge

Blists Hill, Ironbridge Gorge Museum
www.ironbridge.org.uk tel: 01952 433424 Coalbrookdale, Shropshire, TF8 7DQ
Blists Hill Victorian town is one of the ten Ironbridge Gorge Museums which include
the world's first iron bridge, iron foundries, Coalport China Museum, and a recreated
mine. Blists Hill is an reconstructed Victorian working town, complete with shops, a
bank and a public house.

Brooklands Museum
www.brooklandsmuseum.com tel: 01932 857381 Brooklands Road, Weybridge,
Surrey, KT13 0QN Museum of transport, motor sport and aviation. Several iconic
aircraft on display, including the first British-built production Concorde – partly built
at Brooklands. Large collection of cars, and the London Bus Museum contains around
35 buses and coaches, the largest collection of working historic London buses in the
world. Open daily except around Christmas. Admission charge.

Bruntingthorpe Museum
www.bruntingthorpeaviation.com tel: 0116 2478030 Bruntingthorpe Proving Ground,
Lutterworth, Leicester, LE17 5QS Bruntingthorpe Aerodrome is home to the Cold
War Jet Collection including a Handley Page Victor, a Hunter, Canberra, Comet,
Lightnings, Sea Vixen, Buccaneers, Jet Provosts, a Jaguar, a Nimrod MR2, a Sea
Harrier and a 2-seat Jaguar. Open on Sundays only, and on occasional Open Days.
Admission charge.

Cadbury World
www.cadburyworld.co.uk tel: 0844 880 7667 84 Linden Rd, Bournville, Birmingham,
B30 2LU Tells the story of chocolate-making from source to sale, and includes
demonstrations of chocolate making. Pre-booking recommended. Admission charge.

Cheddleton Flint Mill
www.cheddletonflintmill.com tel: 0161 408 5083 Leek Road, Cheddleton, Leek, Staffs,
ST13 7HL Pair of canal-side water-powered flint mills, flint ovens, a period cottage,
canal loading dock, a Robey steam engine, and small museum. Free entry.

TRADE & MANUFACTURE

Cosford Royal Air Force Museum

www.rafmuseum.org.uk/cosford tel: 01902 376200 Cosford, Shifnal, Shropshire, TF11 8UP Huge collection of both civil and military aircraft from most of the great British makers – A. V. Rose, Armstrong Whitworth, English Electric, Gloster, Handley Page, Hawker Siddley, Supermarine, and many others, including the prototype English Electric P1a which evolved into the Lightning, and one of the two surviving TSR-2 fighter-bombers. Admission free.

Frogmore Paper Mill

www.thepapertrail.org.uk tel: 01442 234600 Fourdrinier Way, Hemel Hempstead, Hertfordshire, HP3 9RY The world's oldest mechanised paper mill – the birthplace of paper's industrial revolution. It is still a working paper mill producing around 100 tonnes of specialist grade paper every year on historic paper machines. Guided tours and a hands-on opportunity to make paper in the traditional way.

Gladstone Pottery Museum

www.stokemuseums.org.uk/visit/gpm tel: 01782 237777 Uttoxeter Road, Longton, Stoke-on-Trent, ST3 1PQ Bone china ware was made in the workshops and giant bottle kilns of the Gladstone China Works, the last complete Victorian Pottery factory in the country. Includes collection of sanitary ware, including some made by the legendary Thomas Crapper. Four large bottle ovens dominate the site. Daily demonstrations of bone china flower making, pot throwing and painting. Admission charge

Haynes International Motor Museum

www.haynesmotormuseum.com tel: 01963 440804 Sparkford, Yeovil, Somerset, BA22 7LH The collection includes over 400 cars and motorcycles from all over the world. The site is currently being expanded to increase exhibition space. Open March to October. Admission charge.

Heritage Motor Centre

www.heritage-motor-centre.co.uk tel: 01926 641188 Banbury Road, Gaydon, Warwickshire, CV35 0BJ The British Motor Industry Heritage Trust's collection of over 300 British-built cars chronicling the history of the British motor industry from Albion in 1901 to the last-ever Rover 75 in 2005.

Hendon Royal Air Force Museum

www.rafmuseum.org.uk/london tel: 0208 2052266 Grahame Park Way, London NW9 5LL Collection of over 100 aircraft from some very early designs through to the latest modern-day jets and military aircraft, together with exhibitions and displays of some of the museum's thousands of artifacts relating to the aircraft, aviaition and the history of RAF Hendon. Open daily. Admission free.

Imperial War Museum Duxford

www.iwm.org.uk/visits/iwm-duxford tel: 01223 835000 Duxford, Cambridge, CB22 4QR Vast collection of aircraft past and present. The AirSpace hall tells the story of aviation in Britain and the Commonwealth, with over 30 iconic aircraft including Concorde, TSR-2 and the Spitfire on display. Regular air shows. Admission charge.

TRADE & MANUFACTURE

John Jarrold Printing Museum
www.johnjarroldprintingmuseum.org.uk tel: 01603 677183 Whitefriars Norwich Norfolk, NR3 1SH Collection of 19th and 20th century printing equipment. Demonstrations of printing processes in an historic working print workshop. Open Wednesday am only.

Kidwelly Industrial Museum
www.kidwellyindustrialmuseum.co.uk tel: 01554 891078 Broadford, Kidwelly, Carmarthenshire, SA17 4LW This museum is unique in being the only museum dedicated to an understanding of the tin-plate industry and is sited in an 18th century former tin-plate works. Includes much machinery from the rolling mills, and other artifacts. Open Tuesday-Thursday in summer, weekends in winter. Check website for details.

London Transport Museum
www.ltmuseum.co.uk tel: 020 7379 6344 Covent Garden Piazza, London, WC2E 7BB The Museum's collection was started the 1920s, when the London General Omnibus Company preserved two Victorian horse buses and an early motorbus. The museum is housed in the Flower Market building in Covent Garden and includes buses, trams, and a representative cross section of overground and underground transport in London.

MOSI Manchester
www.mosi.org.uk tel: 0161 832 2244 Liverpool Road, Castlefield, Manchester, M3 4FP The Museum of Science & Industry is housed in five listed buildings including Liverpool Road Station, the world's first passenger station. It covers a wide range of industrial themes focusing on Manchester's contribution to science and industry. The Revolution Manchester gallery, divided into six sections, explores Transport Revolutions, Computer Age, Engineering, Energy, Cottonopolis and the Structure of Matter.

Museum of Brands, Packaging & Advertising
www.museumofbrands.com tel: 020 7908 0880 2 Colville Mews, Lonsdale Road, Notting Hill, London, W11 2AR Based on the world-famous Robert Opie Collection, the museum tells the fascinating story of the emergence of branding. Originally in Gloucester Docks from 1984-2001 as The Museum of Packaging and Advertising, a second museum – Opie's Museum of Memories – opened at Wigan Pier in 1999, before the collections were moved to London to become The Museum of Brands, Packaging and Advertising in 2005.

National Gas Museum
www.nationalgasmuseum.org.uk tel: 0116 2503190 195 Aylestone Road, Leicester, LE2 7QH The museum's collection of objects and ephemera has been described as the most significant collection of material relating to the gas industry, its application and its impact on society in the world. Open Tues/Weds/Thurs afternoons only.

TRADE & MANUFACTURE

National Media Museum
www.nationalmediamuseum.org.uk tel: 0844 856 3797 Little Horton Ln, Bradford, West Yorkshire, BD1 1NQ The museum tells the story of photography, film and television in a series of interactive galleries and exhibitions. The Kodak Gallery tells the story of popular photography from its earliest days. The television galleries explore the development of television, from the first scientific breakthrough in 1877 to the evolution of colour transmissions, recording devices and satellite television. A changing programme of major photographic exhibitions takes place in large galleries. Free Admission.

National Motor Museum Beaulieu
www.nationalmotormuseum.org.uk tel: 01590 614650 Brockenhurst, Hampshire, United Kingdom, SO42 7ZN Housing a collection of over 250 automobiles and motorcycles the museum tells the story of motoring on the roads of Britain from the earliest days to the present time. The admission charge covers entrance to the National Motor Museum, Palace House and Gardens, Beaulieu Abbey and the World of Top Gear.

Newquay Classic Air Force Collection
www.classicairforce.com tel: 01637 860717 Hangar 404, Aerohub 1, Newquay Cornwall Airport, St Mawgan, TR8 4HP A collection of more than a dozen classic aircraft, most still regularly flying. The collection includes an Avro Anson, BAC One-Eleven, De Havilland Dragon Rapide, Vampire and Venom, an English Electric Canberra, a Gloster Meteor, a Hawker Hunter, a Hawker Siddley Nimrod, and a Vickers VC-10.

Robert Smail's Printing Works
www.nts.org.uk/Property/robert-smails-printing-works tel: 0844 4932100 7/9 High Street, Innerleithen, Peebles, EH44 6HA Preserved print works where visitors get a hands-on experience of composing, and demonstrations of printing. Presses still used today for commercial print jobs, including some of the NTS's own literature.

York's Chocolate Story
www.yorkschocolatestory.com tel: 0845 498 9411 King's Square, York, YO1 7LD York is synonymous with chocolate – the Tuke, Rowntree, Terry and Craven families made the city world-famous for its chocolate and sweets – and a one hour tour explores the history and processes of chocolate-making, giving visitors a chance to try their hands at the task themselves.

TEXTILES

Borders Textile Towerhouse, Selkirk

www.museumsgalleriesscotland.org.uk tel: 01450 377615 1 Tower Knowe, Hawick, TD9 9EN A museum to the Borders textile industries, telling the story of wool and tweed, with hands-on exhibitions. Open daily, except on Tuesdays and Sundays in winter.

Cambrian Mill Heritage Centre

www.cambrian-mill.co.uk tel: 01591 610363 Llanwrtyd Wells, Powys, Wales, LD5 4SD A guided tour covers the entire process involved in the production of the fine woollen tweed manufactured and produced at the mill, from the shearing of the sheep, through the cleaning and spinning of the wool, to weaving and final processing. Guided tours available weekdays only.

Coldharbour Mill

www.coldharbourmill.org.uk tel: 01884 840960 Coldharbour, Uffculme, Devon, EX15 3EE A spinning mill built by Thomas Fox to spin woollen and later worsted yarns in 1799, Coldharbour Mill is a rare survival of Georgian architecture and industry. Since reopening as a museum in 1982 the mill has continued to produce high quality worsted yarns and cloths on its period machinery. Power comes from an 1821 breast shot water wheel, an 1867 Kittoe & Brotherhood Beam Engine, a rare 1910 Pollit & Wigzell 300hp Steam Engine and a Lancashire Boiler, still operated on regular 'steam up' days.

Helmshore Mills Textile Museum

www.lancashire.gov.uk/leisure-and-culture/museums/helmshore-mills-textile-museum tel: 01706 226459 Holcombe Road, Helmshore, Rossendale, BB4 4NP Two original Lancashire textile mills, Higher Mill and Whitaker's Mill, are together known as Helmshore Mills Textile Museum. Higher Mill contains a large waterwheel with five pairs of fulling stocks, while Whitakers Mill houses a unique collection of industrial machinery. Open daily mid-February to December.

Lochcarron Mill Visitor Centre

www.lochcarron.co.uk tel: 01750 726100 Dunsdale Rd, Selkirk, TD7 5DZ Working textile factory, and visitor centre. Mill tours introduce visitors to all aspects of tartan production from spun yarns to finished fabrics. A turbine water wheel is also on site.

Masson Mills

www.massonmills.co.uk tel: 01629 581001 Derby Rd, Matlock Bath, Derbyshire, DE4 3PY Sir Richard Arkwright's vast 1783 Masson Mills are the finest surviving and best preserved example of an Arkwright cotton mill. Working textile museum illustrating Arkwright's legacy. Collection of historic textile machinery dating from the 18th-20th centuries. Working machinery demonstrations daily. Open January-November, closed December.

TEXTILES

New Lanark

www.newlanark.org tel: 01555 661345 New Lanark, South Lanarkshire, ML11 9DB
Five-storey cotton mill, built 1784. Originally founded in 1786 by David Dale, the mill
and its community rose to world fame under the guidance of Robert Owen. Now
restored and listed as a World Heritage Site, by 1799 New Lanark was the biggest
cotton mill in Scotland and one of the largest industrial complexes in the world. At its
peak, over 2,000 people lived or worked in the village, and the mill continued
manufacturing cotton until 1968.

Paradise Mill & Macclesfield Silk Museum

www.silkmacclesfield.org.uk/museums/paradise-mill tel: 01625 423883 Park Lane,
Macclesfield, Cheshire, SK11 6TJ Paradise Mill is the centrepiece of Macclesfield's Silk
Museum, where visitors can experience the weaving floor of a working handloom silk
mill, one of the last to close in the town. The original machinery is still operated by
expert guides. In the Silk Museum itself, the story of Macclesfield silk is told through
displays and restored machinery. Museum open Mon-Sat, mill tours daily at 11.45,
13.00 and 14.15.

Quarry Bank Mill

www.nationaltrust.org.uk/quarry-bank tel: 01625 527468 Styal, Wilmslow, Cheshire,
SK9 4LA Five-storey cotton mill, built 1784. Working museum of the cotton industry,
with looms and other machinery, powered by a 50-ton waterwheel and a working
1840s' steam engine. The noise of the heritage machinery and steam engines is
considerable. Exhibitions chart the progression of the cotton industry from mediaeval
times through to the 19th century. The Apprentice House and workers' village are
both nearby.

Queen Street Mill, Burnley

www.lancashire.gov.uk/acs/sites/museums/qsm tel: 01282 412 555 Queen Street ,
Harle Syke, Burnley, Lancashire, BB10 2HX Lancashire's last surviving 19th century
steam powered weaving mill. The 500hp tandem steam engine, *Peace*, complete with
Lancashire boiler, still drives over 300 looms in the weaving shed.

Stanley Mills

http://www.historic-scotland.gov.uk/index/places/propertyresults/propertyabout.
htm?PropID=PL_273&PropName=Stanley%20Mills tel: 01738 828268 Stanley,
Perthshire, PH1 4QE Built in 1786 by a hairpin bend in the River Tay, where
tremendous water-power was available, the mill's machinery was initially powered
by water wheels, later by electricity generated by water turbines. The cotton mill was
built by local merchants, with support from Richard Arkwright, and remains the finest
example of an Arkwright mill. Now in the care of Historic Scotland. Very little
machinery is preserved, but hearing the recorded voices of former workers echo
through the empty mill floors of the restored buildings is a unique
experience. The Bell Mill is one of the oldest surviving in the world.

TEXTILES

Stott Park Bobbin Mill

www.english-heritage.org.uk/daysout/properties/stott-park-bobbin-mill tel: 01539 531087 Colton, Ulverston, Cumbria, LA12 8AX Working bobbin mill, built in 1835 by John Harrison and now restored to working order by English Heritage, Stott Park is typical of hundreds of small bobbin mills which used locally coppiced wood to turn out bobbins for the cotton industry. The horizontal steam engine which drove the mill was built by William Bradley at Gooder Lane Ironworks in Brighouse, and is now steamed on the first weekend of every month, and on Bank Holidays.

Strutt's North Mill, Belper

www.belpernorthmill.org tel: 01773 880474 Bridgefoot, Belper, Derbyshire, DE56 1YD The 1804 North Mill, originally water-powered, is part of the Derwent Valley Mills World Heritage Site. The museum tells the story of cotton spinning and stocking making, and how Belper became one of the world's first factory communities. Working historic machinery captures the atmosphere of a Victorian cotton mill and includes 80 spinning frames with 4236 spindles each, 136 carding engines, 16 drawing frames and 4 stretching frames.

Trencherfield Mill Engine, Wigan

www.wigan.gov.uk/Resident/Museums-archives/Trencherfield-Mill-Engine.aspx tel: 01942 828128 Heritage Way, Wigan, WN3 4EF The largest working triple-expansion mill engine in the world, built in by J. & E. Wood of Bolton in 1907 to power a large spinning mill, the engine is still operational in its original engine house. Now fuelled by bio-diesel rather than coal, and with steam raised in a modern boiler, the engine is steamed on Sundays, with access at other times by arrangement.

Verdant Works, Dundee

www.rrsdiscovery.com/index.php?pageID=130 tel: 01382 309060 W Henderson's Wynd, Dundee, DD1 5BT The Verdant Works is the only working jute museum in the United Kingdom, and is housed in a former jute mill. The museum tells the story of jute production in Dundee – once so important that the city was known as 'Juteopolis'. Demonstrations of jute weaving on historic looms by former weavers.

Whitchurch Silk Mill

www.whitchurchsilkmill.org.uk tel: 01256 892065 28 Winchester Street, Whitchurch, Hampshire, RG28 7AL The mill has been producing silk since 1817, when it was bought and converted by a silk weaver from Spitalfields, and it is now the oldest silk mill in Britain still in its original building. The Georgian mill – the current waterwheel dates from the 1860s – still weaves silk using 19th century machinery. Until the 1890s, when power looms were installed, all silks were woven on handlooms. Handloom weaving has recently been returned to the mill. Open Tuesday to Sunday, admission charge.

INDEX

143